BOOKS BY WILLARD N. CLUTE

FLORA OF THE UPPER SUSQEHANNA.

OUR FERNS IN THEIR HAUNTS.

FERN ALLIES OF NORTH AMERICA.

FERN COLLECTOR'S GUIDE.

OUR FERNS: THEIR HAUNTS, HABITS AND
    FOLKLORE.

EXPERIMENTAL GENERAL SCIENCE.

AGRONOMY.

LABORATORY BOTANY.

LABORATORY MANUAL AND NOTEBOOK.

PRACTICAL HIGH SCHOOL BOTANY.

AMERICAN PLANT NAMES.

A SECOND BOOK OF PLANT NAMES.

USEFUL PLANTS OF THE WORLD.

BOTANICAL ESSAYS.

SWAMP AND DUNE.

OFF THE RECORD (VERSE).

THE
COMMON NAMES OF PLANTS
AND THEIR MEANINGS

By

WILLARD N. CLUTE

SECOND EDITION

WILLARD N. CLUTE & CO.
INDIANAPOLIS, INDIANA
1942

PREFACE TO THE FIRST EDITION

Some ancient worthy, doubtless in a moment of exasperation, has written that "An examination of the common or vulgar names of plants will at once introduce us to a complete language of meaningless nonsense, almost impossible to retain and certainly worse than useless when remembered." Possibly to the unaccustomed ear the common names of plants may sound like "meaningless nonsense," but that they are really so is far from the truth. These are the first names that many plants had. They were given by the common people to indicate the species in which they were interested and, being largely descriptive, contain in their substance, "like flies in amber," an immense fund of plant lore that is quite worth investigation.

In this little book, therefore, I have attempted to unravel a few of the terms that have been applied to the common plants of our fields and woods. To explain them all would require a volume of more than ordinary size and necessitate the work of many years to complete.

Those who wish to go more extensively into the meaning of plant names will find in the pages of *The American Botanist* a series of nearly a hundred articles which give the meanings of all the names in numerous plant families. A "Second Book of Plant Names" recently issued is a further investigation of the subject. A list of more than 12,000 common names of the plants of eastern America, grouped under their proper technical equivalents, but without explanations, will also be found in the third edition of my "American Plant Names."

So far as can be ascertained, the names discussed in the present volume are correctly explained. It may be said, however, that, in many cases, two or even more different explanations of a single term exist, none of them, perhaps, supported by evidence sufficient to make the meaning beyond question. In such cases, I have selected the explanations which to me seem most probable. Readers who do not agree with me will, of course, select such others as suit them better.

In the matter of the technical terms I have followed the well-known "Gray's Manual"

7th edition, thus attaching a standard name to
each plant by which it may be followed through
botanical literature, avoiding the inclusion of
the author-citation for each species which is
of little interest to the general reader.

In the hope that students of plant names
will find as much interest and amusement in
perusing this book as I have had in making it,
I dedicate it to all sincere plant lovers. May
their tribe increase!

Indianapolis. June 30, 1931.

THE AUTHOR.

PREFACE TO THE SECOND EDITION

In making a second edition of this book, I
have taken the opportunity to correct several
small errors in the text and to add new data in
many places. The nomenclature has also been
changed to follow that of Bailey's "Hortus
II," which is in most cases in accord with that
of the first edition but nearer the present ideas
of the subject. The common names, however
have not changed in any particular.

Indianapolis. August 15, 1941.

CONTENTS.

CHAPTER I.

It is probable that the names of plants have interested Man from the very beginning. We have it on the best of authority that one of the first acts of the Original Gardener was to give names to the plants, and his descendants have followed his example, even to the present day. Most of the conspicuous plants now have at least one common name and many have several, but the making of names goes merrily on.

It is natural that plants should have names: without some sort of appellations, we would find it difficult to distinguish them from their associates, to mention them to our friends, or even to think of them clearly to ourselves; but in the opinion of many, the names are altogether too abundant. Some single species have as many as eighty in addition to various others which have been applied to them by technical botanists.

In the beginning, plant names were prob-

1

ably mere assemblages of sounds to indicate
the kinds of plants that interested primitive
peoples—chiefly such species as were fit to
eat, or were poisonous, or medicinal, or useful
for garlands, employed in charms or sorcery,
or used in divination. Those who believe in
evolution may please themselves by thinking
that even our ape-like ancestors began the
naming of plants by originating various
sounds to indicate their favorite forms of
vegetation and to express their dislike of
harmful kinds. At any rate, the word botany
comes from a Greek word, *boskein,* meaning to
eat, and plainly shows what some of the earliest people thought of the study of plants.

Evidently some of our plant names go back
to an era beyond the invention of written
language; back, in fact, to the very beginning
of things. Many of them were hoary with age
before the upstart technical names were invented. In the course of time, inattentive ears
and careless tongues have obscured the
original sound of many, changes in the
language itself have rendered others meaningless, the play of rustic imagination has added
various new ones, ignorance is responsible for

a number of curious errors and for the be-
stowal of plant names on species to which they
do not belong, and other changes have occurred
until the task of discovering the original meanings is far from easy, and in some cases quite
impossible.

The most prolific namers of plants have
always been those in closest contact with nature—farmers, shepherds, fishermen, hunters,
woodsmen, and those ancient herb gatherers
who, wandering far afield in search of the
"simples" which they "compounded" into
medicines, explored every woodland and
thicket. The names given to the plants thus
encountered were usually descriptive of the
haunts in which they were found, the seasons
in which they bloomed or produced their
fruits, their useful properties, their medicinal
virtues, real or imagined, or various other
conspicuous characters. Even today, it is not
uncommon for the plant student, encountering
an unfamiliar species, to recognize it by its descriptive common name—a sincere tribute to
the ability of some ancient observer to select
salient features by which to indicate it to
others.

Among the common plant names referring
to particular habitats are mountain laurel,
swamp saxifrage, wood lily, sand violet, bog
orchid, riverweed, marsh marigold, pond lily,
rock cress, meadow rue, orchard grass, cliff
brake, and field garlic. Naturally plant names
referring to the seasons are more abundant in
the temperate zone than elsewhere, for the
changes there are more marked. In colder regions, the blooming season is so short that all
the plants burst into bloom almost simultane-
ously, while in the tropics the yearlong season
allows them to bloom at their leisure. In the
middle regions, however, the blooming is seasonal, with violets, trilliums, and phloxes at
the beginning, goldenrods, sunflowers, asters,
and gentians at the end, and a host of rose-
worts, legumes, mints, and others scattered in
between. Seasonal names, therefore, are usually full of meaning, such as spring beauty,
summer hyacinth, fall dandelion, autumn crocus, and winter aconite. Of course there are
Mayflowers in abundance, as well as May-
apples and Juneberries, August lilies, October
berries, summer-sweet and winter-bloom. Nor
are special days forgotten, for we have Lent

lilies, Pasque-flowers, Easter lilies, Pinkster-flowers, Michaelmas daisies, Christmas roses, and many others.

Color names are found in great variety, but it is surprising to discover that few if any flowers are named for nature's favorite color —at least the one she uses most lavishly—a combination of purple and red usually known as magenta, but which often masquerades as pink. As a matter of fact, most of the flowers called pink are really magenta. The common "red" clover, for instance, is magenta rather than red, though the crimson clover is true to its name. Among other color-names, are black nightshade, cardinal flower, fire pink, yellow daisy, purple cone-flower, green dragon, white trillium, violet wood-sorrel, blue-bell, and orange hawkweed. We even have such contradictory names as white- and yellow-violets. Many roses are far from rose-colored and such things as white blackberries and blue-berries are well known.

In that part of the United States east of the Mississippi and north of the Ohio, there are upwards of four thousand different kinds of plants, and to these, as we have noted, more than fifteen thousand common names have been attached. It is probable that at least half the number of species in this region are so inconspicuous or so insignificant as to have no common names whatever, which leaves the remainder with an average of more than seven names each. It would be a mistake, however, to assume that all these names are in common use. Undoubtedly the majority are of the kind that have appeared once or twice in literature and thus achieved a questionable sort of immortality in all subsequent lists. It would greatly relieve plant study if some way could be devised for getting rid of all such terms, but alas, once published they are a part of the history of the species and will doubtless continue to be quoted to the end of time.

Through all the naming, moreover, there runs a tendency to ring the changes on any name or idea that happens to strike the fancy. If a plant is associated with the idea of snakes, we may expect to find it called snake-plant, snake-berry, snake-root, snake-leaf, snake-grass, snake-weed and so on. A plant grown in moist places is likely to have water, swamp, pool, marsh, bog, and perhaps several other watery adjectives attached to its group name. It is not surprising, therefore, to learn that the common names are anathema to technical botanists.

Many of the common names of American plants were made abroad—in England, Germany, France and other countries. The very earliest, of course, hail from Arabia and Greece where plants seem to have first made an impression on the observant. These names have become attached to our own plants in a variety of ways. In some cases, the very species to which they rightfully belong have smuggled themselves into our country mixed with garden and field seeds or in the food and bedding of live stock. Or, native plants may bear the names of foreign species because the genera to which they belong have representatives on both sides of the Atlantic, and the joint ownership of the family name has made easy the shifting of common names from one species to another. Many American plants, also, bear foreign common names through the fact that they happen to resemble Old World species for which they have been mistaken. Usually, however, the names of indigenous origin are of far greater

interest. Some of these are due to the exuber-
ant fancy or dry humor of the early settlers,
others are the result of attempts to render into
English the Indian names for the plants, and
still others are popular attempts to indicate
the plants by descriptive titles.

Most exasperating of all are the "English"
or book names which, in recent years, a group
of well-meaning but entirely misguided indi-
viduals have attempted to give to each species
of plant, doubtless hoping that in time there
might be established in our language a single
authoritative term for each species, just as
there is a single correct technical name. But
common names are not made in that way.
They are coined from the thoughts of the common people and spring into being as the need
for them arises. It should be quite apparent,
also, that there are many plants which lack a
common name of any kind and which need
none because the ordinary individual has no
occasion to speak of them. Even though they
possess conspicuous flowers, they are mere
weeds to him and thus mean nothing. In the
majority of cases, however, the "English"
names are worse than useless, being often mere

translations of the technical terms that only add to the confusion of the beginner without advancing the study of plants in any way. It certainly cannot be claimed that such bizarre appellations as auricled otophylla, glaucous anticlea, slender agalinis, and Bull's synthyris, are any more significant than the technical terms they would supplant; or that many still more nonsensical "book" names will ever come into use, of which, Brainerd's cat's foot, Stewardson Brown's Indian turnip, Judge Daly's sunflower, and Miss Mulford's violet, are among the horrible examples.

Although non-technical plant names are usually called common or vulgar names, they are often far from common. People sometimes speak of making a common name, as if it were in the power of anybody to make a name common. In earlier days, such names were often called trivial names, as were the specific technical names also. In books they are often spoken of as popular or country names, that is, names familiar to the people. It is apparent, however, that neither common, trivial, vulgar, popular, country nor "English" quite expresses the idea of names in our own language. Perhaps the idea is best indicated in still another term, vernacular, which is fast coming into use and which signifies names in our mother-tongue.

Apparently Man gave names to plants before he turned to naming the groups of his own species; at least there are many surnames among us derived from plants. In some instances, it is possible that these names have been associated with plants through a similarity of sounds, but that many have been given by design cannot be doubted. The great Linnaeus, himself, owes his name to an immense linn, or linden tree (*Tilia*) which stood on the family acres. From this tree came such family names as Lindman and Lindenman. Two of his great uncles were clergymen and in recognition of their position took the name of Tiliander, also from the great tree. The father of Linnaeus was also a clergyman and adopted as his family name the Latinized form of Lindman, or Linnaeus. When the son of Linnaeus was granted a patent of nobility, he also took the family name and became Carl von Linne. Otherwise he might have remained plain Carl Nilson; that is, the son of Nils Ingemarson.

Among surnames derived from plants are
Abele, Akers, Alders, Almon, Anise, Arnot,
Ash, Aster, Avelin, Basel, Baum, Bay, Bean-
blossom, Beech, Berry, Bracken, Bramble,
Brier, Broome, Brune, Brunel, Brush, Budd,
Bush, Campion, Capers, Caraway, Cedar,
Cherry, Chestnut, Clary, Clover, Cockle, Cof-
fee, Coine, Cole, Colin, Comfrey, Corne, Cor-
nel, Cotton, Couch, Crabb, Crabtree, Cress, Cur-
rant, Daisy, Darnell, Dill, Drew, Elder, Eller,
Eller-bush, Emery, Elms, Fennell, Fern, Fitch,
Flagg, Flaggman, Flower, Furze, Gale, Garlic,
Gourd, Grass, Greenwood, Gribble, Hague,
Harlock, Haugh, Hawthorn, Hawtree, Hay,
Hazel, Heath, Heckathorn, Hedge, Hollins,
Holly, Holm, Hopper, Huckleberry, Ivy,
Kale, Kane, Kemp, Knott, Lavender, Lemon,
Lever, Lichin, Lily, Linden, Linn, Lupien,
Mallowes, Maple, May, Millet, Moss, Mullin,
Nettles, Nutt, Oakes, Oates, Olive, Onion, Pal-
mer, Peach, Pear, Pease, Pepper, Plant, Plan-
ten, Plum, Pink, Poppe, Ramsey, Reed, Rice,
Root, Rowell, Rowan, Rowantree, Rush, Sa-
very, Seed, Seebright, Snooks, Spiers, Spink,
Sprout, Tansy, Thistle, Thorn, Thyme, Towe,
Tree, Turnipseed, Twigg, Vine, Violette,

Ware, Weed, Weld, Whiteoak, Wickens, Wickes, Wood, Woodruff. After naming the plants and later appropriating some of the names for his own family tree, Man turned his attention to giving similar names to the locations in which various conspicuous plants flourished. If we are to believe the records, the family name of Snooks was originally Seven-Oaks, while Quatrefages, the name of another family, is literally four beeches (*Fagus*). Twelvetrees is a cognomen of the same order.

The numerous towns and hamlets to which place names were attached, were undoubtedly named after men had settled there, but whether man gave the name to the place, or the place became a family name, is still far from clear. Good instances of such names are Allerton, Appleby, Ashton, Farnham, Thornton, Brackenridge, Elmton, Birchfield, Beanfield, Beanblossom, Bromley, Ellerfield, and many others. Some of these have re-entered our language to give names to their namers such as Thornton, Linton, Furnside, Crabtree and Whiteoak. Our own country was settled too late to participate very extensively in such name-making, but we have done fairly well in the matter of fruits, having towns bearing such titles as Apple, Orange, Berry, Raisin, Cranberry, Mulberry, Pawpaw, Pear, Pine-apple, Peach-tree, Cherry-tree, Almond, Hazel, Butternut, Walnut, and Hickory.

CHAPTER II.

THE TECHNICAL NAMES.

The young lady who explained that she liked everything about plants except botany probably expressed the sentiment of a great many people. We admire the brilliant colors, pleasing fragrance, and graceful forms of the flowers; we ornament our grounds, decorate our dwellings, and adorn our persons with the choicest specimens; we employ them in profusion for all sorts of festive occasions, and in time of trouble endeavor to express our sympathy and soften the grief of our friends by their use; but when it comes to the study of the science of plant life, most of us show a strong inclination to avoid it.

Much of the aversion to technical botany doubtless comes from the idea that the study deals principally with long and almost unpronounceable names taken from foreign languages and only with difficulty assimilated into our own. That this view of the subject

14

is by no means new is shown by a letter written in 1753 by Peter Collinson to Linnaeus, the "Father of Botany" in which he says:

"I have had the pleasure of reading your 'Species Plantarum,' a very laborious and useful work, but my dear friend, we that admire you are much concerned that you should perplex the delightful science of botany with changing names that have been quite well received and adding new names quite unknown to us. Thus, botany which was a pleasant study and attainable by most men, is now become, by alterations and new names, the study of a man's lifetime, and none now but real professors can pretend to attain it. As I love you, I tell you our sentiments." Later he returns to the subject and adds:

"If you will forever be making new names and altering good and old ones for such hard names that contain no idea of the plant, it will be impossible to attain a perfect knowledge of botany."

Paradoxical as it may seem, the extended use of the common names has made the technical names necessary. In the early days, before even the conspicuous plants had acquired a multiplicity of names, the group names in the vernacular were quite sufficient to indicate the species. But when means of communication multiplied and different localities were found to have different names for the same plant, it became apparent that a more stable means of designating them was needed. It was then that the use of technical names arose. In spite of the greater accuracy of such names, however, the common people have ever shown a predilection for the names in the common tongue.

Scientific terminology, indeed, has been a matter of slow growth. Though many of the common names of plants are group names which indicate relationship, it took plant students a long time to appreciate the fact that plants are really related and can be arranged in groups to show this. It was still longer before they recognized the characters that most unmistakably indicate such relationship. Until this was realized, no philosophical system of naming plants was possible. Our present style of nomenclature, in which each species is given a generic or group name and a specific or individual one, was initiated, if not actually

invented, by Linnaeus the Swedish botanist,
less than two centuries ago. Earlier students
indicated their plants 'by phrase-names consisting of a string of descriptive Latin adjectives. At this time our little walking-fern,
which we now know as *Camptosorus rhizo-*
phyllus, was called *Phyllitis parva, saxatilis,*
persummatatis, folii prolifera, and a little
member of the pink family (*Gypsophila*
fastigiata) was known as *Lychnis alpina, linii-*
folia, multiflora perampla radice. Possibly
the idea that botany consists largely of difficult names originated at this time.

In spite of their forbidding appearance,
there can be no doubt that the technical names
are best for designating species precisely,
since there can be only one correct technical
name for each kind. As for the common
names, a plant may have from one to a hundred or more, and since the species often
ranges beyond state boundaries, some names
may be in a foreign tongue also. Disputes
may arise as to which common name is the
correct one, but this is never the case with the
technical names for all are agreed that the
first name correctly applied shall be the one

and only name of this kind. In practically all
cases the technical names are cast in Latin
form, and when written, the generic or group
name precedes the individual or specific one.
Many of the early technical names were simply
the vernacular name Latinized; in fact, the
common names are themselves based on a sort
of binomial system, in which one name repre-
sents the group and the other the species, as
red clover, day lily, and flowering dogwood.
In such cases, however, the group name is
written last.

Although the fact that the technical names
have been taken from a foreign language is
often deplored, it is probably fortunate for us
that this is the case. One can imagine the confusion that would exist, if Russians, Chinese,
Turks, Arabs, and other nations of the world
(who have as much right to make names in
their own tongue as we have in ours) should
insist on naming their plants in the vernacular. By agreeing that Latin shall be the
language of science, the authorities have
avoided endless confusion. Indeed, we have
not entirely escaped trouble from this source,
for an occasional foreign proper name has

been Latinized with striking results, as in *Kraschennikowia Maximowicziana,* the technical name of a little anemone-like plant found in Russia.

In the beginning, however, Latin appears not to have been deliberately selected for the technical names. It acquired this distinction principally because Latin was the language of the learned at the time that Botany was taking shape as a science. An interesting illustration of the reverence in which Latin was at one time held as a polite language, even in English-speaking countries, is found in the story of the poet, Crabbe, who is reported to have written a work on botany which he carried to Dr. Arnold of Rugby for approval. The learned doctor reported that the ideas were all right, but the one great defect in the work was that it was not written in Latin. This so angered the poet that he burned his manuscript.

One special advantage in the use of Latin for the technical names is that it is a dead language, in consequence of which it is not subject to change as living languages are, and thus the meaning of the words is unvarying, a most important requisite in naming plants and animals. Moreover, although the names may appear uncouth at first sight, they are not as formidable as they seem. We daily use many terms as difficult without protest. This is aptly expressed in a recent book on plants in which the author says, by way of preface, "There are no words in this book more difficult than rhinoceros, rhododendron or chrysanthemum."

Among vernacular names that have been derived from the Latin, we find that the rose was *Rosa,* the violet, *Viola,* and the lily, *Lilium.* Others that have suffered little more from the change are mint (*Mentha*), amaranth (*Amaranthus*), peony (*Paeonia*), and plantain (*Plantago*). On the other hand, a host of technical terms have been adopted bodily into the vernacular and we speak of aster, azalia, hydrangea, geranium, dahlia, phlox, portulacca, gladiolus, galax, coreopsis, spiraea, cosmos, and others, without a thought of their technical origin. Often it is hard to discover whether some of these were first used in the vernacular and later Latinized, or the reverse.

Among the more interesting technical

names are those which recall important per-
sonages, patrons of science, explorers of new
regions and pioneers in the study of plants.
Some of these need no interpretation, as
*Washingtonia, Jeffersonia, Franklinia, Col-
linsonia,* and *Linnaea.* The ancient herbalist,
Fuchs, is honored in *Fuchsia, Lobelia* recalls
L'Obel another European plant student, and
Tragius is the Latinized form of Bock, both
technical and common names referring to the
goat. *Kalmia* is for Peter Kalm who travelled
in America and wrote two volumes about its
plants and other curiosities, *Magnolia* is for
Pierre Magnol, a French student of our plants,
and *Purshia* is for Frederick Pursh who made
many an expedition on foot through the eastern part of our country in the early days in
search of specimens. *Clintonia* is for a famous
governor of New York, digger of the Erie
canal, *Claytonia* honors John Clayton, a pi-
oneer botanist of Virginia, *Mitchella* is for
John Mitchell, a correspondent of Linnaeus',
Torreya is for John Torrey an early professor
of botany in Columbia University, and so on
down the line until all the Fathers of Botany
have been included, ending with *Carnegia* for

Andrew Carnegie, a sort of step-father, since his name has displaced the older generic name of *Cereus* for the giant cactus.

Although our concern at present is not chiefly with the technical terms, it may be noted in passing that these, too, contain a wealth of meaning if one will take the trouble to investigate them. Undoubtedly the technical terms are best when it is necessary to accurately indicate a given species, and they have been so used in this book, but a real vernacular name is as much a name as any other and may be used when no confusion of meaning results. Oak, willow, maple, beech and birch, for instance, are quite as good as their scientific equivalents: *Quercus, Salix, Acer, Fagus,* and *Betula.*

CHAPTER III.

Our oldest indigenous plant names are undoubtedly those that were bestowed on our native species centuries before the advent of Europeans. Although the original inhabitants lived mainly by the chase, they knew of many plants that could be used for food, medicines, or in their domestic arts, and of course had names for them. With many of these the explorers, trappers, and other pioneers must early have become familiar. Lacking names of their own for such species, or perhaps too busy fighting the namers to make new ones, they readily accepted those in common use, adopting them into their own language with only such changes in form as might be expected to occur in the process of naturalization.

Probably all the berries, nuts, and roots that we consider edible were on the Indian's bill of fare, as well as many others that would

23

scarcely appeal to civilized palates. Those
with which the settlers were familiar, or which
were similar to Old World plants, naturally
received the names by which they were known
in the homeland, but those which found favor
only with the Indians seem to have retained
their primitive names. The thick starchy
rootstocks of the arrow-arum (*Peltandra Virginica*), the golden club (*Orontium aquaticum*), and the yellow pond lily (*Nymphaea
advena*) were boiled and thus supplied a
nourishing, if not especially palatable dish.
To this food, they applied the name of *tuck-
ahoe*. In the Delaware tongue this is said to
mean a small round cake and very likely indicates the form in which the food was served.

The arrow-arum was also known as wampee
or wapato and the name is still applied to the
starchy tubers of the arrow-leaf (*Sagittaria
latifolia*), though they are now more frequently known as duck potatoes, in reference
to the wild duck's fondness for them. In the
west, where these species did not grow, the Indians found the thick roots of *Lewisia rede-
viva,* which they called spatlum, an agreeable
substitute. The *Lewisia,* named for captain

Meriwether Lewis of the Lewis and Clark expedition, is represented in many other parts of our country by the little spring beauty (*Claytonia Virginica*) whose small dark tubers have often been used for food and are said to taste like chestnuts.

A thriving Canadian city owes its name of Saskatoon to a Blackfoot Indian term for that group of shrubs or small trees which the New England settlers knew as shad-bush (*Amelanchier*). The fruit, which ripens in June, is quite palatable and is known to many a rambler as service-berry, June-berry or Indian cherry, but on the frontier it is still saskatoon. It was called shad-bush by the settlers along the Atlantic coast because its blooming was supposed to mark the season when the shad ascended the rivers to spawn.

Another aboriginal word still in use for an edible wild fruit is pembina. This seems to be the Indian equivalent for a species of viburnum (*V. trilobum*) whose acid drupes, relished by both Indians and whites, render the English name of highbush cranberry significant. Europe has a species that was once thought to be the same as ours, but its fruits are nauseous and inedible. A sterile form is our well-known snowball tree or guelder rose.

Curiously enough, *sassafras,* which looks and sounds so much like an Indian word, is said not to be of American origin. The original sassafras is a native of Europe, where our plant, *Sassafras albidum,* does not grow. The name is perhaps derived from the Latin *Saxifraga* or saxifrage. No such doubt exists regarding the derivation of poke-weed (*Phytolacca decandra*), that plant which is the basis of the spring dish known to the inhabitants of the Southern States as "poke salad." This plant is certainly the pocan of the Indians and the pocan-bush of the whites. The name is said to be derived from *Pak* an Indian word meaning blood and probably referring to the red juice of the fruit. The word, *pocan,* should not be confused with pecan, another Indian term used by both races to indicate the fruits of *Carya pecan.* An associated southern tree, the persimmon (*Diospyros Virginiana*), bears another familiar Indian name. This is the species whose young fruits take the palm for astringency, but when ripe are beloved by boys, opossums, and raccoons.

A dwarf member of the chestnut family, also native to the Southern States, is known by the Indian name of chinquapins (*Castanea pumila*). It bears nuts about the size of hazelnuts. In the Northern States, the hard, round fruits of the yellow lotus (*Nelumbium pentapetalum*), a member of the water-lily family, are often called water chinquapins or yankapins, the latter being perhaps nearer the Indian word in sound.

The word camass seems to have once been a general term for various edible tubers and bulbs, but in the course of time this has become identified with certain liliaceous plants known as wild hyacinths (*Camassia esculenta*). The name, indeed, has been Latinized as the technical name of the genus. This is one of the few cases in which an Indian name has been adopted by formal science. There is, however, one other which deserves mention. This is *Catalpa,* the name of a handsome flowering tree discovered by Catesby in 1726 in the country of the Catawbas in the Carolinas. The tree is often called catawba-tree, but the tribe which it recalls is more distinctly

honored in the technical specific name of the
rose-bay (*Rhododendron Catawbiense*). We
may also add to names of this character
Asimina, the generic name of our native
papaw (*Asimina triloba*) which is derived
from the Indian name, *Asiminin.*

The Indian *wahoo* is a term applied to a
number of medicinal plants, some of which
have found a place in the materia medica of
civilization. The plant usually regarded as the
true wahoo is the plant often called the burn-
ing-bush (*Euonymus atropurpureus*) because
of its brilliant autumn coloring, but a western buckthorn, the well-known Cascara seg-
rada (*Rhamnus Purshiana*), the cork elm
(*Ulmus racemosa*), and the basswood (*Tilia
Americana*) are also known as wahoo.

What *puccoon* may mean is now something
of a puzzle though it seems to have referred
originally to plants yielding a red pigment.
Possibly this is another term derived from the
Indian *Pak,* meaning blood. The puccoons
are still called by color-names, but most of
these refer to other colors than red. Possibly
the original puccoon was the bloodroot (*Sanguinaria Canadensis*), because of its red juice.

The plant is also called puccoon-root, Indian paint, and white puccoon, the last in reference to its white flowers. For yellow puccoon, we have a choice between the golden seal (*Hydrastis Canadensis*) whose roots are yellow, and *Lithospermum angustifolium* whose flowers are of this hue. A relative of the last mentioned is the orange puccoon, (*Lithospermum canescens*)—in fact, all the plants in the *Lithospermum* genus are occasionally called puccoons.

Still more puzzling is the Cree Indian word *wicopy,* which might be associated with materials for tying, since the name is used for the moosewood (*Dirca palustris*) whose bark is so strong as to gain for it the common name of leatherwood. The strong inner bark of the basswood (*Tilia Americana*) is also called wicopy, but here the resemblances end, for the willow herb (*Epilobium angustifolium*) is also called by this name, as is the calico-bush (*Kalmia latifolia*) and the stagger-bush (*Lyonia mariana*), none of which are known for their strong fibers. Other variants of the name are wicky, wickup, and herb-wicopy.

The various species bearing the Indian

name of *cohosh* are distinguished by medicinal qualities, though they also bear names which indicate color. It is difficult to decide which was the original cohosh. Circumstances however, point to the blue cohosh (*Caulophyllum thalictroides*) for this also bears the name of pappoose-root and squaw-root, and was used in the Indian's materia medica. The black cohosh, used even now by regular physicians, is *Cimicifuga racemosa*, while the two baneberries (*Actaea rubra* and *A. alba*) are the red and white cohoshes, respectively, both members of the buttercup family and possessed of poisonous properties.

While it is true that tobacco came originally from America, it is also true that all Indian tribes did not use this plant for smoking, though most of them possessed other materials that could be used. These were usually referred to by the term *kinnikinnik*. One of the kinnikinniks is still known as Indian tobacco (*Lobelia inflata*), but plants regarded as better entitled to the name are the bearberry (*Arctostaphyllos uva-ursi*), the burning bush (*Euonymus atropurpureus*), the aromatic wintergreen (*Gaultheria procumbens*), the willow (*Salix*), and several species of cornel or dog-wood, especially *Cornus amomum* and *C. stolonifera*.

Various other Indian terms are found in lists of plants but they appear never to have captured the fancy of the settlers sufficiently to be incorporated into our language, though they are quite as musical as the substitutes invented by civilized man to replace them. In spite of our neglect, they go singing on in the books with meanings now perhaps entirely lost. Among them are wickawee, missymoosey, mech-a-meck, tipsinna, uncum-piuncum and pipsissewa.

Though the aboriginal names have largely failed to make an impression on technical botany, they have not altogether failed of adoption into the vernacular. Among plants so named are a number that commemorate Indian tribes, in most cases because they were identified with the tribe in some way, usually from their use. Most famous of these is the Seneca snake-root (*Polygala Senega*) which recalls a once-powerful tribe of central New York. The plant is of real medicinal value and may be found in medical tomes under the name of seneca snake-root or senega-root.

A familiar plant, still used for basket-making and similar purposes, and commonly called Indian hemp (*Apocynum cannabinum*), was once known as Choctaw root. The Mohawk-weed (*Uvularia perfoliata*) is named for another tribe of central New York, while the Apache plume (*Fallugia paradoxa*) is naturally a plant of the desert Southwest. The Chickasaw plum (*Prunus angustifolia*) is a wide-ranging species which covers more territory than was ever covered by the tribe for which it is named, and the Osage orange (*Maclura pomifera*) is a well-known hedge plant. A species of *Psoralea,* otherwise known as Indian bread-root (*P. esculenta*), is the Cree potato.

A more famous potato is the mic-mac potato (*Apios Americana*) whose tubers were undoubtedly the first potatoes to be sent to Europe from our country. The Indians called this plant *Sagabon* and from this Sag Harbor, on Long Island, is said to have derived its name. The tribe that has made the most lasting impression on both history and botany, however, is the tribe of Shawnees. This people originally lived about the Savannah river but later moved to the region north of the Ohio where under a chief named Tecumseh they made things lively for the whites for a considerable time. At least three plants commemorate them: the Shawnee haw (*Viburnum nudum*), the Shawnee salad (*Hydrophyllum Virginianum*), and the Shawnee tree, also called Shawnee wood (*Catalpa speciosa*). The Cherokee rose, commonly believed to be a native of the South and adopted by one State as its representative flower, is not an American at all but is *Rosa laevigata* of China and Japan.

CHAPTER IV.

The pioneers who penetrated into the American Wilderness soon found themselves in contact with a strange people whose manners and customs were quite unlike their own. New foods, new forms of dress, new kinds of dwellings, new remedies for disease, and many novel ways of behavior, served to constantly remind them of the fact. Following a well-nigh universal tendency to relate the name of anything new to the country or people from which it comes, they naturally attached the name Indian to many of the objects they encountered. Our language contains many similar illustrations, among them English sparrow, Spanish onion, French marigold, Norway rat, Italian clover, Russian thistle, German measles, and Greek valerian.

One must make a sharp distinction, however, between names of Indian origin and certain others made by Europeans with reference

34

to the aborgines.   There are upwards of a
hundred names in our flora in which the word
Indian appears, but it is obvious that none of
these are of Indian origin.   Most of them were
given by the settlers to distinguish wild plants,
newly encountered, from similar species in the
homeland, or to indicate those strange plants
which the Indians found useful.   Not infrequently, perhaps, the word Indian was used in
a disparaging sense for species regarded as
less valuable than those in cultivation.

Probably one of the first plants to be named
for the Red Man was the Indian corn (*Zea
Mays*).   It is well known that the corn of the
Old World and of the Bible is not the grain
which we so extensively cultivate under this
name.   In Europe, "corn" means wheat, oats,
rye, or other grains.   When the colonists found
the Indians cultivating a new and taller kind
of grain, they naturally spoke of it as Indian
corn.   Europeans have since learned to follow
the technical botanist in calling our plant
maize, though they still speak of the ears of
corn as corn-cobs.   We, in the country of its
nativity, have shortened the name to corn,
and, like the Indians, base much of our pros-
perity upon it.

It will not do, however, to assume that all plant names with the word Indian in them, relate to the American Aborigines. The Indian chickweed (*Mollugo verticillata*), for instance, is a little mat-plant that came to us from the warmer parts of the world and has no association with America's primitive inhabitants. The Indian strawberry (*Duchesnea Indica*) as its specific name indicates, is certainly entitled to be called Indian, but in this case the name refers to India and we must make the same distinction that the British do, and insist that this at least was not named for the "red" Indians. The Indian mallow (*Abutilon Theophrasti*) is another case of the same kind. It, too, comes from the other side of the world.

Notwithstanding the fact that *Zea Mays* was cultivated by the aborigines long before the advent of Europeans, neither of the names that we now use for it is of Indian origin. The name of Indian corn, as we have seen, was bestowed on it by the English, and maize turns out to be a Spanish name which Columbus gave to the plant when he encountered it in the West Indies. The latter name, however, was an attempt to represent the sound of the

native word for the plant and so may claim
to be at least part Indian.

Among the more useful of the Indian's food
plants are the Indian potatoes (*Apios Americana, Helianthus giganteus,* and *H. tuberosus*). These, even the white man has used on
occasion; indeed, *Helianthus tuberosus* is the
Jerusalem artichoke, extensively cultivated
as a stock food and not entirely disdained by
cultivated human palates. The Indian bread-
roots (*Psoralea esculenta* and *P. hypogaea*)
have not found favor with civilized man but
they provided many a welcome meal for his
wild brother. The Indian turnip (*Arisaema
triphyllum*), though far from being a turnip,
is also edible when boiled. This plant is well-
known for the almost unbearable tingling
sensation left in the mouth and throat when
even a small piece of it is chewed; cooking,
however, removes the acridity and makes it
palatable. A related species of Europe affords
the starch known as "Portland sago." The
May-apple (*Podophyllum peltatum*) was
known to the settlers as Indian apple, but it is
really a berry. It was doubtless relished by
the red man though an unappreciative botan-

ist has recorded that it is "eaten by boys and pigs!"

A number of plants seem to have been associated with the Indian through pure fancy. No fewer than six different plants with bright and conspicuous blossoms have been named Indian pink, doubtless with reference to the Indian's well-known predilection for brilliant colors. These six are *Castilleja coccinea, Silene Virginica, Quamoclit coccinea, Spigelia Marilandica, Lychnis flos-cuculi,* and *Polygala pauciflora.* It required perhaps little fancy to see in the blossoms of *Cypripedium parviflorum,* an Indian shoe or moccasin. Long before the American species was known the resemblance of the flowers of the European species to a shoe had been noticed and the plant named Venus' shoe. The slender cylindrical fruits of the catalpa tree (*C. speciosa*) are often known as Indian beans and Indian cigars. It is doubtful if the Indians ever used them for smoking, but small boys in more cultivated communities often do. Most interesting of all the plants named for the Indians is the Indian pipe (*Monotropa uniflora*) which, in late summer, rises a few inches

above the decaying leaves on the forest floor—
a pure white waxen flower, which in stem and
blossom exactly simulates a tiny pipe.

We cannot imagine a real use by the
aborigines of Indian ginger (*Asarum Canadense*), Indian lettuce (*Pyrola Americana*),
Indian currant (*Symphoricarpus orbiculatus*)
or Indian tea (*Ceanothus Americana*), though
the leaves of the last-mentioned were used as
tea by the whites during the Revolutionary
War, and the Indians may have used them
also. Nor is it likely that the hollow leaves of
the pitcher plant (*Sarracenia purpurea*) were
used as cups by the Indians, though they are
known as Indian cups. Possibly these are
plants mentioned only to their disparagement,
as are most of the species associated with the
word squaw. A few of the numerous squaw-
berries, squaw-weeds, squaw-bushes, and
squaw-roots are edible or medicinal, but the
majority are regarded as worthless. The
squaw-berry (*Mitchella repens*) has brilliant
red fruits, but the interior is dry and tasteless,
and the squaw-huckleberry (*Vaccinium stam-
ineum*) is almost the only species in its genus
that is inedible.

CHAPTER V.

When our country was new, a large number of common names were needed at once to designate the host of strange plants encountered. The settlers could not wait for the technical man with his scientific terms and so named them according to their own ideas. No greater opportunity for making names has occurred since Adam's time, for it was literally a new world and a new creation. The namers naturally began with the names the Indians had invented and added others to the list as occasion required. Usually the names were pretty closely descriptive, for it was necessary that others readily recognize the species indicated; besides, life in the wilderness was too serious a matter to allow of much fancy in the names of plants.

Many plants were easily disposed of by distinguishing them as "wild" in contrast to similar species remembered from the home-

40

land. The list of plants characterized thus is too long to be included here, but it comprises references to most of the familiar plants of the Old World. Another list in which the word "false" is used to distinguish the species is nearly as long. It is but fair to say, however, that in this latter list are included a number of plants quite unlike those with which they were compared. In such cases they appear to have been called false simply to indicate that they were plants of similar nature though perhaps not of similar appearance. On the other side of the Atlantic, plants called wild or false are exceedingly rare.

The plants that were quite unlike those of Europe had, of course, to be named on their merits, and the names they received, though keeping close to the facts, nevertheless show considerable versatility on the part of the namers. Numerous plants were named for their likeness to other things, as the thimble weed (*Anemone cylindrica*) whose rough heads of fruit were very suggestive of green thimbles. The tulip tree (*Liriodendron tulipifera*) was called saddle-leaf because the young leafblades in the bud were bent back across the petiole in such a way as to retard the growth of the tip and make it appear as if cut square across. The twin-leaf (*Jeffersonia diphylla*), with two equal leaflets that make the blade look as if cut in half, almost named itself, but the name of umbrella leaf for *Diphylleia cymosa* was not so fortunate a choice since the leaf of the mandrake (*Podphyllum peltatum*) is much more umbrella-like. Probably the latter failed to receive a name referring to its leaves because the attractive edible fruits held the attention of its discoverers.

The side-saddle flower (*Sarracenia purpurea*) has a round and conspicuous stigma that remains after the flower has faded, like a small umbrella held over the developing fruit, but its resemblance to the cushion, or pillion, placed behind the man's saddle and upon which the women rode in early days, is responsible for the name. The peculiar shape of the stigma is further emphasized in the name of dumb watches by which the plant is also known. The little *Dirca palustris,* with bark so strong that the Indians used it for thongs, naturally became leatherwood and this is still its best known common name.

Though the pinnatifid leaves of *Comptonia peregrina* caused it to be mistaken for a fern, it was so strongly and pleasantly scented as to be distinguished from all fernlike plants by the name of sweet fern. The sassafras (*Sassafras albidum*), with strongly aromatic bark, was called cinnamon-wood, and its spicy relative of the lowlands was spice bush (*Benzoin aestivale*).

The persimmon (*Diospyros Virginiana*) was a new fruit to the pioneers, but they did the best they could under the circumstances and called it date plum. The Indian cucumber-root (*Mediola Virginica*) was more accurately named, for the underground root-stock has a strong flavor of cucumber. The coffee-tree (*Gymnocladus dioica*) was much too harmful to be used as a substitute for coffee, but its hard brown seeds, about the size of coffee beans, make the name appropriate. The baked apple berry (*Rubus chamæmorus*) was edible and well named, and anybody with a sense of smell could have named the carrion flower (*Smilax herbacea*).

The Osage orange is native to the country west of the Mississippi and did not receive a name until some time after explorations were well under way, but, when found, the large orange-shaped fruits were properly named for the Osage Indians. Later, when the thorny plants came to be used as hedges in regions where other fencing material was hard to obtain, it became hedge-apple and by this name it is known to most of the children of the prairie States.

One might be puzzled to know why one species of huckleberry (*Gaylussacia baccata*) is called crackers, cracker-berry, and black-snaps, until in eating the fruit he finds the seeds cracking between his teeth. Other plants with interesting names are fire-weed (*Epilobium angustifolium*), fire cherry (*Prunus Pennsylvanica*), and fire lily (*Lilium Philadelphicum*), all so called because they are among the first to appear in burned over tracts. The willow has always been a favorite material with children for making whistles, but the striped maple (*Acer Pennsylvanicum*) is the real whistle-wood because its bark is so easily loosened in spring when whistles are in season.

In Europe the catchflys are species of pink-worts, but our native catchfly, aside from the insectivorous plants by this name, is one of the dogbanes (*Apocynum androsaemifolium*), whose mechanism for securing pollination is so constructed that it frequently catches small insects by the tongue and holds them fast until they starve to death. It is frequently called by the appropriate name of cruel plant.

Hobble bush is another name that seems quite as appropriate and spontaneous for any plant whose branches take root at the tips and thus trip or hobble the saunterer. The name is especially applied to *Viburnum alnifolium*. Dog-hobble, a name given to *Leucothoe Catesbaei*, refers to its dense growth of tangled twigs which hobbles, or hinders, in a different way. Another appropriate term is shad-bush (*Amelanchier Canadensis*), given to that handsome rosewort which blooms about the time the shad appear in the rivers of the Atlantic Slope. Europeans, unfamiliar with the idea behind the name, are wont to write it shade-bush and possibly wonder how it is shadier than any other bush. The golden-club (*Orontium aquaticum*), whose smooth waxy leaves shed water instantly, is known as never-wets, but the yellow pond lily (*Nuphar advenum*) with floating leaves which are equally smooth is called spatterdocks. Another name for the latter species is brandy-bottle in allusion to the thick, squat seed-vessels.

Occasionally a bit of sly humor has dictated the name of a plant, as when the prickly-looking fruits of the sycamore (*Platanus occidentalis*) are called porcupine eggs, or the red trillium (*T. erectum*) is called bloody nose. Some mischievous botanizer has called *Tradescantia canaliculata,* whose flowers last but half a day, widow's tears because they dry up so soon. A more familiar name is spiderwort, due to the fact that when the stems are broken, the viscid juice is drawn out in slender strands like spider-web. The spiderwort of the gardens is *Cleome spinosa,* named in reference to its long stamens and stalked petals and pistil which render the flower quite spiderlike in appearance.

It seems to be "damning with faint praise" to call the pink-and-white blossoms of the mountain laurel (*Kalmia latifolia*) calico-bush, for it is one of the handsomest of its tribe. A number of composites with yellow rays and dark centers are commonly known as niggerheads, though the more polite term is black-eyed Susan. When the pink inflorescences of *Spiraea tomentosa* appear in the damp meadows, they are so suggestive of church spires as to be known as steeple-bushes, but when the mowers encountered them in their work, they very quickly changed the name to wire bush and hardhack. In some sections the shrubby cinquefoil (*Potentilla tridentata*) is also known as hardhack.

The knapweed (*Centaurea nigra*), which has come to us from Europe, is the Old World idea of hardhack. To this they also give the name of hurt sickle as well as a number of other names indicating its hard character, such as hardweed and iron-weed. Our common ironweed (*Vernonia altissima*) is a tall purple-flowered species growing in fields and meadows and is no doubt quite hard enough to attract the attention of the haymakers anywhere, but various other plants may claim the honor of being the original iron-weed. Probably our species was named in reference to some of these.

CHAPTER VI.

THE CONTRIBUTION OF IGNORANCE.

Travellers in strange countries often make amusing mistakes in trying to express themselves in a foreign tongue. Slight differences in accent or pronunciation may make familiar words meaningless to the natives and give color to the complaint of the tourist that he could not make the people understand their own language. In the matter of unfamiliar names, we are all more or less in a foreign country, and, in spite of our best efforts, new names are made on wrong analogies and false assumptions, while old names may take on strange forms and curious disguises. In this connection we are reminded of the stable-man in charge of a horse named Ajax. The name had no special significance to him and when another horse was added to the stable he promptly rose to the occasion and christened him "Bjax"!

It must have been a cousin at least of this

48

individual who, hearing the Indian tobacco
(*Lobelia inflata*) called lobelia, named a taller
species high belia. No doubt the first term
sounded like low belia to him but, as a matter
of fact, the name has nothing to do with
stature, being derived from L'Obel, the sur-
name of an ancient botanical worthy. The
name of high geranium applied to the well
known shrub, *Hydrangea arborescens,* appears
to be of similar origin. Undoubtedly it was an
attempt of the unlettered to pronounce the
technical name. It is but a step from hydrangea, to hygerangea and then to high geranium.

Not infrequently an inattentive ear causes
the tongue to corrupt even the common names,
making the derivation and meaning twice
difficult. In such cases, mercury becomes
markry, celandine is solentine, vervain is pur-
vain, ranstead is rancid, spikenard is spignet,
mallow is maul or malice, snowberry is canter-
bury, and ginseng is sang. It is probable also
that burnet, the name of a little rosewort
(*Sanguisorba Canadensis*), was originally
only brunette! Strangest of all is terrididdle,
a name applied to the matrimony vine (*Ly-
cium halimifolium*). Upon investigation this

seems to be merely a popular rendition of
tether-devil, though it is still a mystery how
the devil's tether and matrimony are associated! People who make mistakes in even the
common names are probably the same people
who call iris-root orris-root and speak of hy-
brids as high-breeds.

If the ignorant find difficulty in handling
the names in the common tongue, what may be
expected from their wrestling with the technical terms! Who else could have rendered
Tussilago, the generic name of the colt's-foot,
as tushy-lucky, or *Paulonia* as Napoleons. On
the tongues of such folk, *Angelica* becomes
Aunt Jericho, *Datura* becomes dewtry, and
Catalpa, patalpa. There is even a strong
suspicion that Alexanders, applied to *Thas-
pium aureum,* may be a disguise of *olusatrum,*
the specific name of a celery-like European
species which our plant resembles.

Guelder rose, a common name of the snowball bush (*Viburnum opulus sterilis*), is said
to be properly elder-rose, while Virginia tea
is a transposition of the technical name, *Itea
Virginica.* Samphire, (*Salicornia Europaea*)
is really Saint Peter's herb, for it is mani-

festly derived from *Herbe de San Pierre!*
Possibly its only connction with St. Peter,
however, is because it grows on rocks and the
name, Peter, means a rock! In the same way,
species of *Ruppia maritima* have been called
zherbes, though the designation was originally
des herbes. Harping Johnny (*Sedum purpureum*) is the word orpine reduced to the vernacular. Orpine, it may be noted, is a yellow pigment and though our plant does not have yellow flowers, it comes from a race of yellow-
flowered species and gets its name through
this strange series of transfers.

But the illiterate have no monopoly of mis-
pronounced words—or mis-spelled words for
that matter. In the early days, the rules of
orthography, if there were any, were little
revered and each writer seems to have spelled
largely to suit himself. Josselyn, a famous
early traveller in New England, wrote the
name of a common vegetable cultivated by the
Indians as squontersquashes and Roger Wil-
liams, from the same locality, spelled it asku-
tasquash. It will be perceived that these
words are no other than the equivalents for
our modern word squash. It is not surprising,

therefore, to learn that there are at least fifteen ways of spelling persimmon, ranging
from pessemin and pitchamin to pessimon,
puchamine and parsemena.

One might expect that the nurseryman, being so continuously associated with plants,
would be above criticism in the matter of pro-
nouncing plant names, but he is often one of
the worst offenders. The plurals of names
that happen to end in *s* are always a stumbling
block to him. In the case of narcissus and
gladiolus, he takes refuge in the Latin plural
to get out of a bad corner, and calls them
narcissi and gladioli, though narcissuses and
gladioluses are quite correct. He naturally
calls his cactuses, cacti, but not quite daring
to call his crocuses croci, he assumes that
crocus is both singular and plural. The same
is true of iris and phlox. Apparently he
never heard of phloxes and irises. And when
he encounters a word that is both singular and
plural, he inclines to make a new singular, as
when he calls a single species a *specie* or one
plant of *Cosmos* a *Cosmo!* Several species of
loosestrife were so called from an ancient legend that they preserve from strife, but when

another species with rosy flowers was introduced into cultivation, it was promptly called rosy strife. Encouraged by these successes, we find the nurseryman translating *Lonicera bella* as the bell-honeysuckle! A more popular error in which we all seem to have fallen consists in regarding the word cherry as the singular of *cherys* or *cerise,* as the French name it. Cherys is from Kerasos, its place of origin, and seems once to have been both the singular and plural of our familiar fruit. In the same way, bracken seems to be the ancient plural of the fern we call the brake. Nor is pea the singular of pease, though we invariably use the word thus.

It does not follow that because the technical names are pronounced in a certain way the common names follow the same rule. Technically our summer-flowering bulblike plant may be Gladi-olus but the common name is certainly gladio-lus or better gladiole but never gladiola. Ar-butus is correct for the technical name of the New England mayflower, but when used for a common name it is properly arbu-tus. It may well be a question whether or not it is best, in some cases, to deliberately mispronounce the technical names. *Achillea,* for instance, the name given to the yarrow in honor of Achilles, is accented as Achille-a but conveys more meaning when pronounced Achil-lea. Many, also, will learn with surprise that *Anemone,* the name of a genus of spring wildflowers, is correctly pronounced to rhyme with Annie Mony, though this is far from the way in which it is usually pronounced. When one is using the common name, however, anem-one is quite correct.

An interesting little plant of sand barrens, in both Europe and America, is known as bearberry (*Arctostaphyllos uva-ursi*). Some have suggested that the plant should be bare-berry in allusion to its place of growth, but both of its technical names refer to the bear. The plant is medicinal, though it is not likely that bears resort to it. Those who collect it for market, knowing nothing of scientific terminology, call it universe vine. This would be meaningless but for another common name, uversy, in which we discover still another variation of the specific name uva-ursi. This latter is the name by which the pharmacist knows it.

The common St. John's-wort of old fields
and dusty roadsides has the generic name of
Hypericum. This the herb-gatherers have
changed to percum-leaves. Still another
vernacular name for the plant is tutsan which
proves quite a puzzle but is almost certainly
toute saine, equivalent to the English all-heal.
This inference is further borne out by its other
common names of touch-and heal and balm-of-
warrior's wounds. Mistakes in translation
may also make strange names, as in the case of
the sainfoin (*Psoralea onobrychis*) in which
the translator mistook *sain* for *santa* and so
called the plant holy hay, when its real meaning is safe or good forage.

CHAPTER VII.

The activities of the name-tinkers, who feel called upon to supply a vernacular name for each plant whether it needs one or not, are deplored by all students of botany, for a deliberately manufactured name rarely has any significance and simply clutters up the study of nomenclature without adding anything thereto. Popular taste seems to demand that the common names, at least, shall mean something and those of no significance usually fail to be adopted. There are times and circumstances, however, when the necessity for new names results in terms that are both spontanous and appropriate. This seems to be the case with reference to a little yellow-flowered plant known as caltrops (*Tribulus terrestris*). This produces small fruits with sharp projections, much like the ancient caltrops, those devilish spiked balls which were dropped in the rear of a retreating army in

56

the hope that they would lame the horses of pursuers. Our caltrop is fond of growing along desert roadsides and other waste places where the fruits may come in contact with the tires of automobiles, greatly to their detriment. It has now become puncture-vine and automobile-weed with every indication that these manufactured names, like the fruits, will stick.

Still another instance of the making of an appropriate new name is found in the terms applied to the orange hawkweed. When the reddish dandelion-like blossoms of this immigrant began to paint our roadsides, the poetically-minded called it Diana's paintbrush, but when it strayed further afield and began to bother the crops, the farmer opined that it was the devil's paintbrush and so it has remained.

During the first World's Fair, in Chicago, the standing cypress (*Kochia scoparia*), with foliage that turns scarlet in autumn, was largely used for decorations. In spite of the fact that it had half a dozen common names already, those who were attracted by its trim shape and brilliant coloring began to speak of it as the World's Fair plant, and thus a new vernacular name was added to the list. A prickly relative of the World's Fair plant, the saltwort (*Salsola kali*), invaded America a generation or so ago and spread to the waste places where it became known as the Russian thistle and Russian cactus, though not closely related to either cactus or thistles. When growing, the plants assume a spherical shape and in autumn they cut themselves free from the roots and go rolling away before the wind as tumble-weeds. We have several tumble-weeds of our own, notably the winged pigweed (*Cycloloma atriplicifolia*), and the witch grass (*Panicum capillare*), but *the* tumble-weed is *Salsola*.

A considerable number of manufactured names refer to the localities in which the species so named grow naturally, such as Canada ginger, Virginia anemone, Carolina poplar, New England aster, Kentucky coffee-tree, Carolina allspice, New Jersey tea, Ohio buckeye, and Kansas sunflower, but the Canada thistle is a libel on our northern neighbor. The plant is not native to Canada but belongs to the Old World. It has recently spread west-ward and is now known in some sections as

California thistle, a good illustration of the way in which names are made and transferred. It has the distinction of being one of the few plants against which several State laws have been directed—with no great success.

Most of the made names for plants have been given to European species which have invaded our country, but occasionally the situation is reversed and foreign people have had to name some of our weeds anew. The harmless little ditchmoss (*Anacharis canadensis*) found in every aquarium, moved to Europe some time ago and began to fill up the slow-moving streams, whereupon it received the names of American weed and Babington's curse, the latter name for the man who is said to have accidentally introduced it.

The sentimentalists have also tried their hand at making names for species that happen to please them. To this nobody can object, so long as they are not foisted on us as genuine vernacular names. Occasionally, however, some of these more poetic appellations happen to be so appropriate for the species indicated, or so expressive of the sentiment suggested by the plant, that they instantly become popular. One could scarcely imagine a better name for *Dicentra cucullaria* than Dutchman's breeches, since the racemes of flowers quite resemble the breeches of some fat little sprite hung out on a line. Equally appropriate is bleeding heart for an allied species of the Old World—*Dicentra spectabilis*.

John Robinson's name of Christmas fern for *Polystichum acrostichoides,* and Clara Smith's Jack-in-the-pulpit for *Arisaema triphyllum* seem likely never to be displaced in popular favor, while boulder fern (*Dicksonia pilosiuscula*), a name given to a species that loves to wreathe the boulders on stony slopes, has slowly been substituted for the more cumbersome and less descriptive fine-haired mountain fern. Squirrel-cups, though apparently more expressive than any other for one of our early wildflowers, the hepatica (*Hepatica Americana*), has failed to be accepted, and John Burrough's trout lily never has been able to supersede adders tongue or dog-tooth violet for the species of *Erythronium,* except in books. Perhaps the latter failure is because the trout, in many localities, may be less familiar than the flower likened to it. Good

morning Spring, a poetic name for the ubi-
quitous Spring beauty (*Claytonia Virginica*)
is another name that failed to take root.

The dog-fennel (*Anthemis cotula*), which
bears several other names of a derogatory
nature, may as well have chigger-weed added
to the list, though the pestiferous insects it
suggests are far too numerous to be blamed on
one species of plant. With even less reason,
the little Shortia (*S. galacifolia*) has been
dubbed Oconee bells, and the pipewort (*Eri-
ocaulon decangulare*) named hat-pins. The
last, in fact, has lost what little meaning it
ever had, by a change in the fashions.

A number of other species have vernacular
names that are far from literal but nevertheless are so applicable that they are commonly
used. Silver-berry (*Elaeagnus argentea*) is
an attractive name for a fruit covered with
silvery scales, and silver-button is scarcely
less appropriate for the small heads of the
pearly everlasting (*Anaphalis margaritacea*).
Silver-rod is at least a distinctive name for
the only white species of golden-rod (*Solidago
bicolor*), and the name of silver-bell tree
(*Halesia Carolina*) is usually sufficient to

distinguish it from its companions. The black locust (*Robinia pseudacacia*) is sometimes called silver-chain, but with no such appropriateness as golden-chain is applied to the laburnum (*Laburnum anagyroides*). The hard ripe seeds of the honey-locust (*Gleditsia triacanthus*) emit the most delightful squeaks when twisted under foot on a hard surface, as any mischievous schoolboy is aware, and in his vocabulary are known as squeak-beans.

The name of mad violets given to the plants usually called shooting stars (*Dodecatheon meadia*) has all the ear-marks of being a made name, though it is suggestive, for the reflexed petals make the flowers appear as if they were laying back their ears as some animals do when angry. The plant is not a violet, however, nor is its relative, the cyclamen, which if often known as Persian violet. Among other names that seem to be more fanciful than real are rabbit-bells for *Crotalaria rotundifolia,* doll's eyes for *Actaea alba,* honey-balls for *Cephalanthus occidentalis,* and night caps for *Anemone nemorosa.*

More appealing names are moonshine for the silvery-white *Anaphalis margaritacea,* pussy-toes for the soft fuzzy *Antennaria plan-taginifolia,* beard-tongue for the pentstemons whose fifth stamen is covered with hairs, and bible-leaf (*Chrysanthemum balsamita*) for that fragrant plant whose leaves were often carried to church in bibles in the early days, in the hope that their fragrance might keep the owner awake through the long sermons. The yellow blossoms of *Lysimachia terrestris,* shining in low grounds, are appropriately swamp candles, and the globular flowers of the yellow pond lily (*Nuphar advenum*) riding on the water are yellow lanterns. The wafer ash (*Ptelea trifoliata*) is not an ash, but the fruits are like wafers and may suggest other objects, as the additional name penny-tree clearly shows.

The name of obedient plant, applied to *Physostegia Virginiana,* fairly suggests itself, for the blossoms may be pushed in any direction and will retain this pose for a long time. On windy days the flowers all turn in one direction and seem traveling down the wind.

The most widely used of all the deliberately made names is passion-flower, which indeed, has given the technical name, *Passiflora,* to the genus. It is said that the discoverers of the first passion-flowers hesitated to describe them in their books for fear the accounts of this strange flower would not be believed. In the blossoms the explorers fancied they saw displayed many things connected with the Crucifixion. The five stamens suggested the five wounds, the three carpels were the three nails, the tendrils were the scourges, the corona with its many narrow divisions was the crown of thorns, and the ten parts of the perianth were the ten apostles with Peter and Judas left out for obvious reasons. One of the handsomest of the passion flowers is found in most of the region south of the Ohio river, but it is no longer regarded as emblematic of the Crucifixion. The natives call it May-pop in reference to its small, very fragrant, melonlike edible fruits which are also known as wild apricots.

CHAPTER VIII.

It is not to be expected that the common people will invariably recognize the family characteristics of the wild flowers so plainly apparent to the botanist, or distinguish between closely resembling though unrelated forms. Even the more discriminating still call a number of plants roses, lilies, and violets, though fully aware of the fact that they have no claims to such distinctions. In this case however, the fault is not entirely due to a misapprehension, for in the early days the terms were more loosely used than at present. It thus happens that the dame's violet (*Hesperis matronalis*) is not a violet, the day-lilies (*Hemerocallis*) and the water lilies (*Nymphaea*) are not lilies, and the rock rose (*Helianthemum*), the rose of Sharon (*Hibiscus Syriaca*) and the wind-rose (*Papaver argemone*) are not true roses.

In other cases, natural mistakes have be-

65

stowed the name of certain plants on totally different species. One of the first instances of this kind was concerned with the little creeping heathwort which the Pilgrims called May-flower and which we commonly call trailing arbutus (*Epigaea repens*). This last name was given for a fancied resemblance of its blossoms to those of the strawberry tree (*Arbutus unedo*) of Europe, but the two are not closely related. As a further indication of how readily a likeness suggests new names, it may be pointed out that the arbutus-like *Abelia grandiflora,* recently introduced into our gardens, is known as trailing arbutus bush!

We have no true laurels in this country, though there are several plants that bear the name. In this case some of our rhododendrons and kalmias with thick glossy evergreen leaves have been mistaken for laurels. Even the trailing arbutus is occasionally called ground laurel. Another set of transfers is connected with the myrtles. In spite of the fact that the true myrtles lack representatives in our flora, several plants have been named myrtle from their general likeness to the classical myrtle of Europe (*Myrtus communis*). First of these is the periwinkle (*Vinca minor*), a low spreading evergreen plant called running myrtle, whose very name recognizes its distinctness from the real myrtle by the use of an adjective. Some obtuse observer has transferred this name to the creeping moneywort (*Lysimachia nummularia*) whose sole claim to it is found in its roundish leaves. A most un-myrtlelike plant is the common sweet flag or calamus (*Acorus calamus*) though it is often known as sweet myrtle. A little shrub with fragrant leaves and wax-covered berries, from which Christmas candles are often made, is the wax-myrtle or bay-berry (*Myrica cerifera*). These names, however, nearly reduce the plant to a myth, for it is certainly not a myrtle and it cannot be bay-berry, for the word bay, itself, means berry.

All the trilliums are American plants, but the vernacular name most frequently heard for them is wake-robin, a term which is not only transferred from Europe but is transferred from an entirely different group of plants. The Old World wake-robins are plants of the Arum family, related to our Indian turnip (*Arisaema triphyllum*). These latter

plants are also known as dragons abroad, and
the name has become attached to some of our
own species, notably the green dragon (*Arisaema dracontium*), a cousin of the Indian
turnip.

The awe-inspiring title of enchanter's nightshade (*Circaea lutetiana*) has been bestowed
on a small and retiring member of the evening
primrose family. Originally this was the
name of a truly noxious species of Europe,
such as might be employed by a progressive
enchanter, but it is no name for our harmless
species and it is ever a puzzle as to how the
two were confused in the popular mind. Nor
is the European mandrake (*Mandragora*) any
pattern for our mandrake or May-apple (*Podophyllum peltatum*). The foreign plant was
regarded as an awesome species, so powerful
that its roots were formerly carved into the
form of puppets and carried about as charms
against disease and other ills. To secure the
root, however, great cunning had to be exer-
cised, for when pulled up, the plant was said
to emit such shrieks and cries as to deafen
and make mad any who heard them. The accepted method of obtaining the root was to

tie a dog to the plant and then call him from a safe distance.

It is a question whether the name of thorn-apple, applied to a number of trees in the rose family, is a transfer from abroad or whether it arose independently as a good descriptive term. Certain it is, however, that the European plant which bears the name is a poisonous species of the nightshade family (*Datura stramonium*) while ours are the familiar thorny trees with small apple-like fruits found along every country roadside. The fruits are often known as haws; thus the name of thorn-apple as well as hawthorn is explained.

The name of sycamore, applied to a common and well known tree of river-bottoms, has had more than one transfer. Originally it was the name of the wild fig, probably the kind of tree that Zaccheus ascended on a memorable occasion. In the sacred dramas of the Middle Ages, according to Prior, a large leaved maple was selected to represent the fig, and the plant on this account has since been called the sycamore maple (*Acer pseudoplatanus*). When another large tree with maplelike leaves was discovered in our flora by the settlers, although it was easily seen that it was neither sycamore nor maple, the resemblance was enough to make it a good substitute for the sycamore anyway. The English primroses do not grow wild with us, but we have a group of plants with round, yellow or white flowers to which the name of primrose has been transferred. To indicate a difference between the two, our species are known as evening primroses (*Oenothera*), though many of them bloom by day.

One thing that has facilitated the transfer of names is the fact that the floras of America and Eurasia are closely related and probably had a common origin. There are more than two hundred and fifty generic vernacular names that are common on both sides of the Atlantic. With a perennial supply of adjectives, the possibilities of making new names is practically limitless, and yet, in many cases, the names of European species have been transferred directly to the plants in our flora which resemble Old World species and have thus contributed not a little to the "meaningless nonsense" with which the study of common plant names is supposed to be invested.

A very different group of transferred names are those that have been shifted about in our own flora with a full realization of the differences that exist between the plants whose names are thus exchanged. All that is needed is a single characteristic suggesting another species, and with a convenient adjective a new common name is made. The running birch (*Chiogenes hispida*) is a heathwort, but its aromatic leaves make it a birch on the popular tongue. A small shrub with ash-like leaves and prickly stems, belonging to the rue family is almost invariably known as prickly ash (*Xanthoxylum Americanum*).

One sometimes has to be on his guard in gathering berries or he may mistake the astringent pomes of the chokeberry (*Aronia*), for the sweet and edible berries of the huckleberry (*Gaylussacia*), but one taste of each is enough to indicate why the aronias are often called choke-huckleberries. Although we have heathworts in plenty, the heather is rare or missing with us, but a little heather-like plant of sandy regions is a good substitute under the name of beach heather (*Hudsonia tomentosa*). In northern forests, the ground is often covered with the dark, spreading, evergreen branches of the yew (*Taxus canadensis*). This plant we usually call ground hemlock after a more noticeable evergreen of our own, being unfamiliar with the European yew-tree.

Practically the only claim certain western plants have to the term sagebrush is the fact that they have whitish aromatic foliage, similar to that of the true sage. The sage-brushes, however, are Composites, while the true sages are species of the mint family. The entire list of such transfers is too long to be included here, but we may add the ground cherry (*Physalis*) which is not a cherry, the prickly elder (*Aralia hispida*) belonging to the ginseng family, the cucumber tree (*Magnolia acuminata*) named for its fruits which suggest cucumbers, the water willow (*Dianthera Americana*) an acanthus, the horse gentian (*Triosteum perfoliatum*) belonging to the honeysuckle family and unrelated to the gentians, and the Carolina allspice (*Calycanthus floridus*) with no close associations with the tropical spice of that name.

CHAPTER IX.

In spite of much education, the human mind clings to its ancient superstitions. To be sure we no longer hang crabbed old ladies as witches, or believe much in ghosts and goblins, but in out-of-the-way places the elderly inhabitants still carry horse chestnuts in their pockets to ward off rheumatism and tie red threads about the necks of their children to prevent nose-bleed. In this more sophisticated age, we have abandoned the belief in the "mystic fern seed" which would render its possessor invisible, give him the strength of twenty men, and enable him to extort money from the devil. We have relegated to the realms of fancy the moonwort's power to "unshoe the new-shod steed" and even the wonderful spring-wurzel or opening-root, which would loosen any lock if merely placed in the key-hole, seems to have lost its potency, though the magic with which it was once in-

73

vested lingers in the "open sesame" of the tale of Ali Baba and the Forty Thieves.

Along with these beliefs has disappeared the practice of naming plants for saints and heroes in the hope of gaining their favor. This practice was once common, and, as late as the time of Linnaeus, we find him protesting against it. In an old list of British plant names, we find more than eighty referring to the saints and sixteen more referring specifically to St. John, sixty-one referring to Lady and seventeen others that specify Our Lady, fourteen that include the name of Mary, and seventeen more named for the Virgin—a total of two hundred and five, while our own flora contains but a paltry thirty-one names of this nature and most of these are imported.

In explanation of our lack of indigenous plants named for the saints, it must be said that by the time the early settlers had adjusted themselves to the new land and found time to look about them and invent names for the strange plants and animals they encountered, it was rather too late in the history of the subject to do much for saints, gods, dragons, and other mythological creatures. To be sure, witches and goblins had considerable vogue, and the devil, as usual, was conspicuous by his works, but the pioneers were too busy in wresting a living from a stubborn soil to give much credence to a belief in fairies, fauns, nymphs, dryads, and other pleasant, though imaginary, creatures of field and wood. The really indigenous plant names that savor of such beliefs have doubtless been given by poetically minded ramblers with nothing more serious in their thoughts than to supply the plants with what they felt to be appropriate names.

Naturally the Queen of Heaven leads in the number of plant names given in her honor, but even here it is necessary to make a fine distinction between Our Lady and the word which indicates femininity in general. When the term is Our Lady, the meaning is clear enough, but unless the others are supported by fact or legend, they must often be doubted. Such terms as lady's lint (*Stellaria holostea*) and lady's clover or sorrel (*Oxalis*) appear to have been given to indicate soft or delicate plants only. Among the plants certainly referring to the Virgin are the blessed thistle or Lady's thistle (*Cnicus benedictus*) whose specific name supports this conclusion. Still another Lady's thistle is *Silybum Marianum* with a specific name which also shows the intent. Other names for this species are Lady's milk and Virgin Mary's thistle. Lady's thumb (*Polygonum persicaria*) is so named to explain the dark markings on the leaves which are reputed to be the marks of Our Lady's thumb. On the other hand, lady's mantle (*Alchemilla pratensis*), lady's smock (*Cardamine pratensis*), lady's ear-drop (*Impatiens biflora*), lady's purse, (*Capsella bursa-pastoris*) and many others have a more mundane origin, though some may have been named because of their blooming at Lady-tide. Nor do lady's tresses, as commonly supposed, refer to woman's "crown of glory" but to the more prosaic ladies' traces with which the feminine world anciently were wont to compress their waists. The name is now applied to species of autumn-flowering orchids (*Spiranthes*).

A similar state of affairs attends the plant names referring to Mary. Marigold is probably named for the Virgin, but rosemary (*Rosmarinum officinalis*) comes from *ros,* dew and

marianum the sea and really means dew of
the sea. Nor do all the names with the word
virgin in them refer to the Virgin. Virgin's
bower (*Clematis Virginiana*) was named by
Gerarde because, as he said, it was "fit for
the bower of a virgin." The name of
Lady's-slipper also has a most interesting
history. The genus *Cypripedium,* to which
the lady's-slippers belong, was, as its technical name indicates, anciently dedicated to
Venus whose earlier name was Cypris. The
generic name therefore, clearly means Venus'
shoe, but when the European world turned
to Christianity, it was thought to be perhaps a bit impious to call the plant after a
heathen goddess and so it was renamed Our
Lady's slipper. Unfortunately the technical name was not converted and while the
world at large has settled down to calling the
plant Lady's-slipper, the scientific name continues to bear witness to the fact that it is
Venus' shoe. We have a number of other
plants named for Venus in our flora which
escaped the notice of the devout entirely,
among them the Venus' comb (*Scandix
pecten-veneris*), Venus' pride (*Houstonia*

angustifolia), and Venus' looking-glass (*Specularia perfoliata*). The name of Venus' flytrap (*Dionea muscipula*), given to a little insectivorous plant of the Carolina marshes, has all the ear-marks of a manufactured name, since the bearer is a strictly American plant, discovered long after Venus ceased to be held in special honor.

It is to be observed, too, that not all the saints' names given to plants were designed to honor the saints with whom they are associated. Many have no more significance than comes from the fact that the plants so named are in bloom on or near the saint's day. Possibly this was as convenient a way as any to remember the plant's time of bloom, or perhaps it was the other way around and the blooming plant was a reminder that the saint's day was at hand. In an earlier day when calendars were rare the time of blooming of flowers was of more significance than at present. Other species, however, were named for the saints under whose tutelage they were supposed to be and in consequence were regarded as possessing great potency in curing diseases. It is quite likely that a plant which was found

to relieve certain illnesses would in time come
to be associated with the particular saint reputed to be a protector from such ills, especially if it bloomed on the saint's day.

None among the saints is more highly regarded than St. John the Baptist and none
has a greater number of plants named in his
honor.   His chief associations are with
warmth and light, and his festival, the 24th
of June, is near the summer solstice. He is naturally the banisher of darkness and the foe
of evil spirits.   Numerous plants with bright
flowers which open about midsummer have
been dedicated to him.   St. John has often
been identified with Baldur, the Norse sun-
god, and, one by one, the plants formerly
dedicated to that god have been transferred to
him.   A genus of yellow-flowered plants, the
St. John's-worts (*Hypericum*), are regarded
as his special charges and therefore potent in
curing disease and affording protection from
evil spirits.   A common species of old fields,
Hypericum perforatum, was the original *fuga
daemonum,* but as regards its reputed power
to protect from the devil, it may be mentioned
that a well known legend accounts for the

numerous clear dots in the leaves of this plant
by the assertion that they represent perfora-
tions made by the devil with a needle.

As in other cases, saint's names have been
attached to various indigenous species through
sheer fancy. This is probably true of St.
Jacob's dipper (*Sarracenia purpurea*) and
St. Joseph's wand (*Pentstemon acuminatus*).
Our St. Peter's wort (*Ascyrum stans*) and the
St. Andrew's cross (*Ascyrum hypericoides*)
are scarcely better situated since they are not
the original plants so named but are obliged
to bear names transferred from European
species. Our filbert, however, appears to
have been named for St. Philibert, but for
what reason legend is silent, though possibly
because the nuts ripen about the saint's day.

Although our flora can boast of but few
saint's names of any significance, we have a
large number of technical names referring to
heathen gods and goddesses as well as numerous names commemorating more or less
legendary kings and heroes. These were all
given oringinally to Old World species. A
technical name once adopted, however, cannot
be changed, and while the common names may

vary or disappear entirely with the passing
years, the technical terms, permanently en-
shrined in scientific terminology, will continue
to remind us of a time when the world was
young and all the gods were close at hand.

It would require more space than can be
spared to enumerate all the technical names of
this kind, but we may instance the nymphs
Calypso and *Arethusa,* remembered in the
names of two bog orchids, and *Atropa,* the
name of one of the Fates, now bestowed appropriately on a deadly species of the nightshade
family. *Centaurea* is named for one of the
centaurs, *Paeonia* for Paeon, a lengendary
physician, and *Achillea* for the well-known
hero, Achilles. *Andromeda* is a marsh plant,
but, unlike her prototype, is not chained to a
rock. *Artemesia* is for Artemis, the huntress
identified with Diana, whose other name, *Cyn-
thia,* is also attached to a genus of plants,
while *Iris* still mirrors the rainbow in its
flowers of many hues.

A milkweed genus, *Asclepias,* is named for
Aesculapius, the god of healing, the loosestrife
genus (*Lysimachia*) recalls Lysimachus,
ancient king of Sicily, and germander (*Teu-*

crium) commemorates Teucer, the legendary
founder of Troy. The gentian (*Gentiana*)
derives its name from Gentius, king of Illyria,
and the bonesets (*Eupatorium*) bear the name
of Eupater, king of Pontus, who is credited
with the discovery of their medicinal qualities,
and so the list goes. Even Adam and Eve have
been remembered, but such names as Adam's
flannel (*Verbascus thapsus*) and Eve's darning needle (*Yucca filamentosa*) must have
been invented after the pair left the garden;
at least they apparently had no use for flannel
and darning needles earlier.

CHAPTER X.

From the fact that our list of vernacular names contains fifty-five referring to the devil, eighteen connected with dragons, and ten more relating to witches, while only thirty-two are named for the saints, it is clear that the enemy of mankind and his cohorts should have a chapter of their own. In names of this kind, our country may be said to be more fortunate than Europe where at least seventy names refer to the devil. Considering the behavior of some nations, however, this is perhaps what one might expect. Europe offsets this record to some extent by eighty-one saint's names. As a matter of fact, they have more saints than devils in their flora while our situation is quite the reverse; for we have twice as many devils and witches as saints.

As might be inferred, all the plants regarded as being connected with the father of evil have strong and distinguishing characteristics, though not all are of an evil nature. There are, for instance, the various devil's bits and devil's bites, *Chamaelirium luteum* and *Liatris scariosa* especially, whose names, to the initiated, carry no implication of harmful qualities; on the contrary, they entitle them to much consideration. These have rootstocks or other parts that end as if bitten off, and the explanation is that they were once so powerful in relieving the ills of distressed humanity, that the devil bit off the medicinal end for spite. Some verisimilitude is given the story by the fact that several of these plants now lack any medicinal virtues whatever. The original devil's bit seems to have been the Old World *Scabiosa sueccia,* but any plant with a blunt rootstock will probably fit the legend as well. Our own *Aletris farinosa* is one of the few devil's bits still used in medicine, from which fact one derives the idea that it must have been powerful indeed before any of its virtues were subtracted by the Evil One.

Most of the plants named for the devil are supposed to resemble him in some way. The devil's tongue, for instance, is the prickly pear (*Opuntia*) whose flat spiny joints are sufficiently devilish to justify the name. Another thorny species is the devil's walking-stick or devil's club (*Aralia spinosa*). Singularly enough, this same species is called angelica tree in some localities! Thorny species seem naturally to merit being named for the devil. On this account, the thorny *Smilax rotundifolia* is commonly known as the devil's hop-vine and the unicorn plant (*Martynia annua*), whose fruits end in two curved hooks, is the devil's horns. The devil's tether (*Polygonum convolvulus*), however, is devoid of thorns and is otherwise known as climbing buckwheat. So weak and slender a vine is much too weak to bind the devil and, if used as a tether, it is small wonder that he is so often found at large. Possibly, however, the name was bestowed on the plant by some irascible botanist who had become entangled in its numerous and wide-spreading stems. This seems all the more probable because another species of bindweed (*Convolvulus sepium*) which forms tangled mats over other vegetation also bears the name. But how the elephant's foot (*Elephantopus tomentosus*) deserves the name of devil's grandmother is hard to conjecture. It must be recorded, also, that various species of spurge, especially *Euphorbia helioscopia* and *E. peplus,* with a milky juice usually regarded as poisonous, are known as devil's milk.

Devil's shoestrings a name applied to the strong slender roots of *Tephrosia Virgini-ana* which often bothered the plowman when breaking new ground was doubtless given in a moment of exasperation. A kind of milk-weed with climbing stems, *Gonolobus gono-carpus,* is less appropriately called by the same name. The devil's apple is often reputed to be the plant which we call the mandrake (*Podo-phyllum peltatum*). This, however, is a case of mistaken identity. Our plant, though quite harmless, happens to resemble the poisonous mandrake of Europe (*Mandragora*) and thus unjustly bears the disparaging name. The prickly seed-pods of the jimson-weed (*Datura stramonium*) are also called devil's apples. The plant we call the prickly poppy (*Arge-mone Mexicana*) is the species often known as devil's fig. In this case, the devil is obliged to gather his figs from thistles, which is more than fallible humans can do.

It is not always poisonous or prickly qualities that incline us to associate various plants with the devil. Those which especially bother the farmer are likely to be consigned to the devil or to his place of abode by the hard-pressed agriculturist. Among these are the blue devils (*Echium vulgare, Lactuca Canadensis* and *Aster azureus*). The white devils is, or are, *Aster lateriflorus*. One of the hawkweeds (*Hieracium aurantiacum*), a rampant weed which paints many an old field a brilliant red, is well-named the devil's paint-brush, and the devil's spoons are the oblong leaves of the harmless water plantain (*Alisma plantago-aquatica*) which are not fairly deserving of the name. Lastly, there are a number of plants named for the devil because they are regarded as a protection against his wiles. All of these seem of Old World origin. In our own country, nothing of the kind has been found that is an absolute protection!

Of the plants known as hell-weeds, or hell-roots, we may mention the lesser broom-rape (*Orobanche minor*), the clover dodder (*Cuscuta epithymum*), the buttercup (*Ranunculus arvensis*) also known as devil's claw, and the

flax dodder (*Cuscuta epilinum*), which also
bears the inelegant name of devil's guts.

As for the dragon, there are enough parts
represented in our flora to pretty nearly re-
construct such a monster. There are two
dragon-heads (*Dracocephalum parviflorum*
and *Prunella vulgaris*)—but of course some
dragons are supposed to have two heads—and
also a false dragon-head (*Physostegia Virginiana*), a dragon's tail (*Arisaema dracontium*), dragon's blood (*Geranium Robertianum*), Dragon's claws (*Corallorhiza maculata*),
two dragon mouths (*Arethusa bulbosa* and
Antirrhinum majus), and a dragon's tongue
(*Chimaphila maculata*). And, now, after
assembling these parts, we find we have three
entire dragons in addition—the green dragon
(*Arisaema dracontium*), a brown dragon
(*Arisaema triphyllum*), and a water dragon
(*Caltha palustris*). It is not likely that any
plant was named for dragons because of an
actual belief in the existence of such creatures
or the connection of plants therewith. Mostly
the names have been suggested by some
fancied resemblance of the flowers or other
plant parts to purely imaginary monsters, as

in the case of the snap-dragon (*Antirrhinum*) whose ripe seed-pods look like dragon's snouts.

In spite of our once popular belief in witches, there are apparently no strictly indigenous plants named for these horrendous creatures. The plants that bear such names have come to us from the Old Country, and even then, the names are often open to other interpretations. The American witch-hazel (*Hamamelis Virginiana*), which reverses the year and blooms in November, instead of spring, may seem to be an exception to this statement, but the plant was probably named for its pliant twigs. The original spelling was wych, or wice. Some, however, insist that our plant was named for real witches because the twigs have been used as divining rods. This is doubtless a tale invented by some ancient dousterswivel intent on investing his performances with greater mystery and importance. The term wych-wood applied to *Euonymus Europaeus* seems to be another case of this kind. Witches' money-bags, on the other hand, may really refer to witches, since the name indicates the leaves of *Sedum purpureum,* in which, by proper manipulation, the lower epidermis may be loosened and inflated to form a pouch. The witch hobble (*Viburnum alnifolium*) may also allude to witches, though the long and pliant stems, which often root at the tips and thus hobble more substantial creatures, are probably responsible for the name. The witches' pouches (*Capsella bursa-pastoris*) are the seed-pods of the plant usually known as shepherd's purse, but the specific name indicates that they really belong to the shepherd instead of to the witch. The witch-bells (*Campanula rotundifolia*) and the witches' thimbles (*Digitalis purpurea*) are both of European origin, though often found with us, and are not as significantly named as many other Old World plants which bear similar names.

We must not overlook other plants associated with the devil, which might be skipped because their names are, in a measure, camouflaged. In the vernacular, "old man" is often a polite way of referring to the devil. Old man's whiskers (*Geum cilatum*), old man's beard (*Chionanthus Virginica*), and possibly the old man's flannel (*Verbascum thapsus*), also, merely suggest an elderly gentleman, especially as *Chionanthus Virginica* is also

known as grandfather graybeard. Several of
the puff-balls (*Lycoperdon*) are called old
man's snuffboxes. The origin of these names
is now so far obscured by the mists of the past
that we may never know whether they refer to
men or devils. The plant called old man (*Artemisia abrotanum*) certainly has no connection with the devil and of course neither has
the old woman (*Artemisia absinthium*).

CHAPTER XI.

An unusual number of plants in our flora bear common names referring to animals, but this is not surprising when we remember that plants and animals are universally associated: indeed, the plants are the only food producers in the world and either directly or indirectly supply food to all other living things. Plants named for animals often indicate merely that plant and animal are to be found in the same habitat, but more often the name has been given to the plant because it serves as food for the animal or suggests in some part, a resemblance to it. Incidentally, it may be pointed out that many animals are named for plants, and that in a number of cases these are the only names they possess. Among insects, one may instance potato bugs, asparagus beetles, corn-borers, elm-leaf beetles, cotton-boll weevils, and tomato-worms. Then there are cedar birds, thistle finches, nut-crackers, tree-spar-

rows, rice-birds, and wood-peckers, as well as
tree-toads and fruit bats. Other examples will
readily come to mind.

On the other hand, the list of plants named
for animals supposed to feed on them is a long
one. Among them may be noted, partridge-
berry (*Mitchella repens*),duck-meat(*Lemna*),
chickweed (*Stellaria media*), bird cherry
(*Prunus Pennsylvanica*), duck-potato (*Sagittaria latifolia*), bear-berry (*Arctostaphyllos
uva-ursi*), bee-balm (*Monarda didyma*), and
bird-seed (*Lepidium Virginicum*). No fewer
than ten different species bear the name of
pigeon berry.

In spite of the fact that the dog is regarded
as man's most faithful friend and companion,
nearly all the plant names that refer to him
are of a derogatory nature and either indicate
worthless qualities or spurious claims to perfection. There are nine dog-berries in our
flora, none of them edible, and four dog-fen-
nels, all coarse and homely weeds. In all, there
are nearly a hundred plant names referring to
the dog and five more that mention hounds,
and in all the list we fail to find any of a com-
plimentary nature. And even if the name

should sound less abusive than usual, we shall probably discover that it has been derived from some other word and does not refer to the dog at all. The names of some of the dog-woods, for instance appear to have been corrupted from dag-wood or dagger-wood in allusion to the use of the wood for skewers to hold meat together in cooking. This seems probable when we reflect that the ability to hold fast is one of the chief characteristics of both dogs and dogwoods. The original dag-wood or dog-wood was probably the Old World *Euonymus Europaeus,* but the name has been passed on to our native *Euonymus atropurpureus* and related species. These plants bear such additional names as skewer-wood, spindle-tree, and peg-wood, additional evidence for the derivation of the name from a term that does not mean dog.

In searching for some other reason for naming these plants for the dog aside from their holding qualities, we find the suggestion that the leaves were once used in making a tea used for washing mangy dogs, but if the leaves were ever so used, it is not likely that the occasions were numerous enough to impress the name on the plants. We may perhaps follow Parkinson, who, speaking of the European dog-wood, says "We for the most part call it dogge-berry tree because the berries are not fit to be given to a dogge." The hound's tongue (*Cynoglossum officinale*) is undoubtedly named for its smooth leaf, like a dog's tongue, but an ancient herbalist reports of it that "It will tye the tongue of houndes so that they shall not bark at you if it be laid under the bottom of your feet."

The American plants most frequently called dog-wood are species of *Cornus,* the one regarded as most warranted in bearing the name being the flowering dog-wood (*Cornus florida*). Though there are a number of Old World species of *Cornus,* these are rarely called anything but cornel in the homeland. Our dog-woods, however, seem to have been frequently mistaken for species of *Euonymus,* which they in some measure resemble, and to have derived their names from them.

Other species besides the cornels that are often called dog-woods are the bird cherry (*Prunus Pennsylvanica*), the bittersweet (*Solanum dulcamara*), the hobble-bush (*Vi-*

burnum alnifolium), and the buck-thorn (*Rhamnus frangula*). There is also a swamp dog-wood (*Ptelea trifoliata*), a pond dog-wood (*Cephalanthus occidentalis*) and a false dog-wood (*Acer Pennsylvanica*). The adjectives in these names indicate that the plants have been confused with the true dog-woods, perhaps from a similarity of appearance, or possibly from sheer inattention and ignorance. Many plants have thus been named for others through honest intent to get at their true identity.

While on the subject of dog-woods, we must not overlook the poison dog-wood (*Rhus vernix*), which is a species of sumach and one of the very few American plants that are poisonous to the touch. Among species certainly named for the dog are the dog-rose (*Rosa canina*), the dog-tansy (*Potentilla anserina*), the dog-elder (*Viburnum Americanum*), and the dog-laurel (*Leucothoe Catesbaei*). The last three mentioned are mis-applications as far as their generic names go, for they are neither tansy, elder, nor laurel.

It is not uncommon in plant names for a term to indicate very different things when

applied to different plants. The butterfly-pea
(*Clitoria mariana*), for instance, refers to the
shape of the blossoms which are fancied to
resemble butterflies; in fact, the entire group
of pea-flowers is often known as the Papilion-
aceae from the Latin *papilio,* meaning a but-
terfly.   The butterfly-weed (*Asclepias tuberosa*), on the other hand, is so named from the
fact that it is beloved by butterflies.   When
the fritellaries are on the wing, one may often
take a dozen specimens with one sweep of his
net over a blooming plant of this species.   The
bee-weed (*Aster cordifolius*), and the bee
balms (*Monarda didyma* and *Melissa officinalis*), derive their names from the fact that
bees favor them.   The last named is also known
as honey-plant, the technical name bearing out
the fact that it is attractive to bees, for *melissa,* the technical name, means a bee.

The names of our larger domestic animals
are often used as adjectives to indicate unusual size or coarseness in plants, though the
line that separates these from names of a
derogatory nature is often exceedingly tenu-
ous.   The horse and bull are frequently selected
to indicate the coarser forms, just as they have

been used to indicate other animals larger than common, as bull-bat, horse-mackerel, bull-frog, bull-head, and horse-mussel. Occasionally such naming extends to inanimate things and we speak of a horse-fiddle or a horse-laugh. Anybody who has tasted horse-radish will testify to its oversized pungency. Similarily, horse gentian (*Triosteum perfoliatum*) is a coarse plant that resembles the true gentians in some respects, horse mint (*Monarda fistulosa*) is a large species of mint, horse-sorrel (*Rumex acetosella*) is a coarse kind of sorrel, horse nettle (*Solanum Carolinense*) has thorns calculated to make the ordinary nettle envious, and so on for more than thirty other species.

There are also a number of horse-weeds but these are no larger or weedier than others. They take their names from growing in places frequented by horses or because horses feed on them. It is not certain whether or not the horse chestnut (*Aesculus hippocastaneus*) was used to indicate a chestnut larger than common or because it is reputed to have been given to sick horses as a medicine. In any event, the ancient name was *Castanea equina*.

The horse has no monopoly of plant name-sakes indicating coarseness. The bull, the ox, the cow, and the ass have their full share of such appellations. The bull daisy (*Chrysanthemum leucanthemum*), which is also called ox-eye daisy, is one of the largest and commonest of daisies, the ox-balm (*Collinsonia*) is merely a larger balm, the cow-lily (*Nuphar advenum*) is a coarse relative of the water-lily, the bull thistle (*Cnicus horridus*) is one of our thorniest thistles, the cow-parsnip (*Heracleum lanatum*) is an immense plant of the parsley family, and the bull rush (*Typha latifolia*) is a giant rush. Concerning the last-mentioned there is some difference of opinion. Some think it a corruption of pool-rush, but either name is not unwarranted. We have briers innumerable, but horse-brier and bull-grip (*Smilax rotundifolia*) are reserved for a kind of smilax whose power to stop and hold the unwary traveller is well known.

Plant names referring to the hog seldom indicate size, but they almost invariably designate worthless or inferior plants. There are, for instance, three kinds of hog-weeds, all vile

weeds. The hog-fennel is another name for
the familiar dog-fennel (*Anthemis cotula*), the
hog-plum (*Prunus Americana*) is an inferior
kind of plum, the hog cranberry (*Empetrum
nigrum*) an inedible fruit, the hog-potato
(*Stenanthium graminium*) a poisonous lily-
wort, the hog-peanut (*Amphicarpa monoica*)
an insignificant trailing plant, and the hog-
apple (*Podophyllum peltatum*) a fruit which
is little esteemed except by children. The sow-
thistles (*Sonchus*) are disagreeable weeds, and
the pig-potato (*Apios Americana*) and the
pig-weed (*Chenopodium album*) share in the
general disagreeableness.

Nearly all plant names referring to the
buffalo have been given from the fact that
they are prairie plants that grow in regions
once inhabited by the animal named. It is
not at all likely that the buffalo ate the buffalo
pea (*Astragalus caryocarpus*), the buffalo currant (*Ribes aureum*), the buffalo berry (*Shep-
herdia argentea*), or the various nuts, beans,
weeds and apples which bear his name. The
buffalo grass (*Bouteloa dactyloides*) and the
buffalo clover (*Trifolium reflexum*), however,
were named for more practical reasons. The

buffalo-bur (*Solanum rostratum*), whose fruit clings to the coats of animals, comes rightly by its name. It doubtless perfected its trick of catching hold of all sorts of animals by practicing on the buffalo. The buffalo nut (*Trapa natans*), however, is an inhabitant of watery places and has nothing to do with the buffalo, except that the hard black two-horned fruit has considerable resemblance to the head of the animal.

Soft and delicate species are often named for animals whose fur is equally soft or who possess other attributes of daintiness. Of this nature are rabbit-bells (*Crotolaria rotundifolia*), pussy-toes (*Antennaria plataginifolia*), and rabbit's foot clover (*Trifolium arvense*). One must not assume, however, that all names of this kind refer to soft and delicate objects. Pussy-toes, indeed, hints of the soft downy flower-heads, but catnip or catmint (*Nepeta cataria*) is so called because cats are fond of it; not merely the house-cat, but also the great cats of warmer regions. There are at least a score of other names referring to the cat but scarcely worth including here.

The hare's colewort (*Sonchus oleraceus*) is

reported to derive its name from the belief
that the March hare is cured of its madness
by eating it. One ancient writer says of it
"Yf a hare eate of this herbe in somer when
he is mad, he shal be hole." Another version
has it that "When the hare is fainting with
the heat, she recruits her strength with it."
Still another legend is that the hare, when
sheltered by this plant, is safe from its
enemies. Such tales, however, are probably
founded on nothing more substantial than the
fact that the plant is a tender species relished
by hares and rabbits. It was once known as
Lactuca leporina, which means essentially
hare's lettuce.

A number of names that appear at first
glance to refer to animals turn out to be quite
otherwise. Swallow-wort, for instance, when
applied to *Asclepias tuberosa,* refers to the use
of this plant as a remedy for quinsy and other
throat ailments that make swallowing difficult.
Another name for it is pleurisy-root, which
also refers to its medicinal virtues. The Old
World swallow-wort is *Chelidonium majus*
which is supposed to open its flowers when the
swallow arrives in spring and to fade when

the bird departs in autumn. This species is
also represented in our flora by plants that
have migrated from Europe. The individual
who named the skunk's cabbage (*Symplocar-
pus foetidus*) had ample reason for his choice
of a name, but it was the unusual odor of the
bruised foliage that suggested it, rather than
the thought that skunks are fond of it or are
found in the watery wastes in which it grows.
Among the few plants named for the arach-
nids are the spiderworts (*Tradescantia*)
which, as we have already noted, have a
mucilaginous sap that appears like spiderweb
when the stem is pulled apart, and the spider-
flower (*Cleome*) named from the long and
sprawling stamens like spider's legs.

It may be questioned whether the crow-
berry (*Empetrum nigrum*) was named for the
color of its fruits or from the fancy that crows
eat it. Other names of this nature are more
easily interpreted. A western species of
pedicularia (*P. groenlandica*) is known as red
elephants, from the curved and projecting
carpels of the red flowers. *Chelone glabra*,
whose pale flowers produced in late autumn
have considerable resemblance to the head of

a reptile, is in consequence called turtle-head and snake-head. Bug-seed (*Corispermum*) is named from its resemblance to a bug and the tick-seed (*Coreopsis*) has a striking likeness to a tick, though people unacquainted with this resemblance often call it stick-seed and imagine the name refers to the way in which the fruits cling to one's clothing. It may be added in passing that several technical terms also refer to insects. The Latin name of the castor bean (*Ricinus*) refers to its buglike seeds, while *Croton* is a Greek name of the same significance, and *Cimicifuga* is literally bug-chaser. Moth mullein (*Verbascum blattaria*) is so called because of its soft petals like a moth's wings and hairy stamens like its legs, but the specific name means a cockroach!

The horse-fly weed (*Baptisia tinctoria*) receives its name from the belief that the fresh branches attached to the harness will keep the flies away from the horses. It is often hung up in the house to drive away flies. It is a mooted question whether the cranberry (*Vaccinium macrocarpon*) is really crane berry because it grows in places frequented by cranes, or whether the term is derived from *cran*, which means a marsh. Perhaps bird and plant were both named for the marsh, though the dictionaries fail to bear out the suggestion. Crane, indeed, is from the Greek *geranos,* the same word from which springs our modern word geranium. A similar difference in translation occurs in the name of the cranberry's companion, the buck-bean (*Menyanthes tri-foliata*). Although the plant is commonly called buck-bean, it has often been suggested that it was originally bog-bean. Certainly it seems more likely to be related to bogs than bucks.

Goose-grass (*Potentilla anserina*), to judge from its specific name which is derived from *anser* the Latin word for goose, is correctly named, but goose-berry (*Grossularia*) apparently has nothing to do with the bird. It is not even a corruption of gorse-berry, as often suggested, in allusion to its prickly stems, but is said to come from the Flemish *Kruys,* meaning a cross, and referring to the triple spines at the nodes. The word may also be related to the German *Krauselbeere* which has been changed in the French to *groseille,* hence *Grossularia,* the technical name. The fly honeysuckle (*Lonicera Canadensis*) appears to bear an insect's name, but this seems due to a misunderstanding of the original meaning. The Dutch word *vlai* or *vly* means a swampy place that dries up in summer, in which situations the honeysuckle is found growing. The original species is the European *Lonicera xylosteum*, but the name was early transferred to one of our native species.

When it comes to plants named for their resemblance to parts of animals, we have enough for a fair-sized menagerie. In such a list, the king of beasts naturally comes first, and we find two related species known as lion-hearts (*Dracocephalum parviflorum* and *Physostegia Virginiana*). *Anemone pulsatilla* is the lion's beard and *Leonurus cardiaca* the lion's ears. The generic name of the last mentioned, however, means lion's tail and this indeed, is another vernacular name of the plant. Heads or tails often seem all the same to the namers of plants. One of our autumn snakeroots, *Prenanthes serpentaria,* is known as lion's foot but *Alchemilla pratensis* is the pedelion, which name is very apparently only lion's foot in disguise. The lion's mouth is *Anterrhinum*

majus, and the lion's tooth is *Leontodon au-
tumnalis*—at least the generic name indicated
as much, but we must not overlook in this connection the dandelion (*Taraxacum officinale*),
which is really the *dent-de-lion* of the French,
and therefore as everybody can see, another
lion's tooth. The old specific name for this
plant was *dens leonis.*

It would be tiresome to list all the other
plants that by their shape suggest animals or
parts of animals. There are no fewer than
seven mouse-ears referring to plants with
small leaves. There is a cat-tail (*Typha*), a
mouse-tail (*Myosurus minima*), a lizard tail
(*Saururus cernuua*), and a number of horse,
mare, and colt's tails. The cat's ear is *Hypo-
chaeris radicata,* the bear's ears *Habenaria
orbiculata,* and the turtle's head *Chelone
glabra.* The bear's foot is *Polymnia uvedalia,*
but what particular foot should be associated
with *Tussilago farfara* is hard to determine
for among its vernacular names are ass's foot,
bull's foot, sow-foot, horse-foot, foal-foot, and
colt's foot. The last name is the one commonly used in medicinal works, but the others

serve as good examples of the way common names multiply, once they get started.

We have not overlooked the names that refer to snakes, toads, and other reptiles, but these are so numerous that they deserve a separate chapter.

CHAPTER XII.

Ever since that memorable encounter with the serpent in the first garden, Man has been strangely fascinated by all sorts of snakes. This fact doubtless accounts for the large number of plant names referring to them. There are more than fifty such names in our flora and half as many more that specify that most fascinating of serpents, the rattlesnake. In addition we have numerous names referring to toads, vipers, frogs, adders, and other creatures which share the general repugnance with which snakes are generally regarded. Our countrymen, however, appear to be a bit jumpy on this subject, for, in contrast to our record, there are less than a dozen plants named for snakes in all Great Britain, and of course none in Ireland.

Many plants have received names of this kind for the same reason that we give disagreeable names to things we do not like. Often

109

they have scant reference to snakes and merely indicate inferior or undesirable qualities. There is a widespread belief that plants which grow in dim and watery habitats are prone to harbor noxious animals, especially snakes, and many a plant has thus acquired an unmerited reputation through growing in damp shades. As a matter of fact, most serpents avoid wet places. In our flora, there are three snake-berries, four snake-flowers, three snake-grasses, and five snake-weeds. As for snake-roots, there are at least twenty-five in the list, each as much entitled to the name as any of the others.

In a few cases, the plants seem to have been named for their reputed power to prevent or cure the bites of serpents, though the majority merely embody the idea that serpents are associated with them. A few of the snakeroots have been found to have real medicinal virtues, though not in connection with the cure of serpent's bites. This is true of the Seneca snakeroot, (*Polygala senega*), Sampson's snakeroot (*Psoralea pedunculata*), and De-Witt's snakeroot (*Prenanthes virgata*). All of these have long held a place in the *materia medica.* The first-named, indeed, is that apotheosis of snakeroots, the rattlesnake-snakeroot, and DeWitt's snakeroot has the distinction of belonging to a genus all of whose species may be called snakeroots on occasion. With such medicinal plants should be included the serpentary (*Aristolochia serpentaria*) whose specific names, both technical and vernacular indicate a connection with serpents.

Of rather more interest are the plant names which indicate some real or fancied resemblance to the serpents themselves. Thus the little orchid, *Pogonia ophioglossoides,* though called snake-mouth, has a technical name meaning like a snake's or adder's tongue. The real adder's tongue probably is a little fernwort—*Ophioglossum vulgatum.* The name has in some way been transferred to the plant we commonly call the dog-tooth violet (*Erythronium Americanum*), though the plant is neither violet nor true adder's tongue. There is some reason, however, for giving the name of adder's tongue to this species, in that the flowers rise from a pair of mottled leaves that are quite suggestive of the patterns in snake-skins. The name of dog-tooth violet still persists, however, because both bulbs and petals are shaped like the holding teeth of a dog. In this connection it will be recalled that the spore-cases of one of our ferns are borne in spikes that so strongly suggest the rattles of the rattlesnake that it is commonly known as the rattlesnake fern (*Botrychium Virginianum*). Among other rattlesnake plants of this nature must be included the rattlesnake plantain (*Goodyera pubescens*), whose dark leaves, mottled with white, like the markings of some snakes, justify the name. The hawk-weed (*Hieracium venosum*) with purple-veined leaves is another rattlesnake plant.

Since the rattlesnake does not occur in the Old World, all plant names suggesting this particular serpent have been made in America and nearly all of them have been given to plants with parts that rattle in the wind. In Europe such plants are usually called rattle-weeds, rattle-boxes, rattle-pods and the like, but with us, it was inevitable that they should become rattlesnake weeds. One exception to this, however, must be made: our plants in the genus *Crotalaria,* which name is derived from the Greek for rattle, have escaped, curiously enough, being named for our famous serpent. *Crotalaria sagittalis,* with pods that rattle attractively is frequently known as rattle-box or rattle-weed. Among others that rattle without reference to serpents is the rattle-pod (*Ludwigia alternifolia*), the rattle-bush (*Baptisia tinctoria*), and the rattle-box (*Rhinanthus cristi-galli*).

We have no fewer than five species known as rattlesnake-masters, but none of them, so far as known, are able to justify the epithet. The plant most commonly known by the name is a coarse yucca-like umbellifer of low grounds, whose technical name is *Eryngium aquaticum.* It is likely that some of the rattlesnake-masters derive their name from the belief that they are able to drive away serpents rather than to cure their bites, but even this distinction is denied them in these more matter-of-fact days.

None of the plants named for vipers seem to have any close association with such animals. The little blue-flowered *Echium vulgare* is known as viper's grass, viper's bugloss, adder's meat and adder's wort, but it is a harmless sort of plant that deserves none of these names. As a prickly weed in cultivated fields, it is more commonly known, to the farmer at least, as blue devils. Another adder's flower, with no reason for being so named, is *Lychnis dioica,* and the little chickweed (*Stellaria holostea*) is another adder's meat. It has been suggested that in some cases the word *attor,* which means poisonous, has been translated to mean adder though it has no reference to serpents.

The useful and phlegmatic toad has several plants named for it simply because they grow in the shady places frequented by toads, or because they are not of much account. The toad-rush (*Juncus bufonius*) is common along meadow paths where, in the evening, toads may be expected, and the toad-flax (*Linaria vulgaris*), with flowers like yellow snapdragons, is a flax-like plant of no value for spinning. Still the "toad" in this name may not refer to the toad at all, but may come from tod, meaning a clump or tuft. The toad-sorrel (*Oxalis stricta*) is simply an insignificant weed whose name was probably derived from wood sorrel! The toad-lily, however, is the white water-lily (*Nymphaea odorata*), apparently named from the belief that toads frequent it. The frog lily (*Nuphar advenum*) is better named, for frogs delight to rest on its round floating leaves. The only really characteristic name relating to toads is toad-bellies, applied to the leaves of *Sedum telephium* and allied species. These, under proper manipulation, may have the under epidermis loosened and, when inflated with air, present an appearance which the common name accurately describes.

CHAPTER XIII.

In spite of the fact that a large number of our plant names indicate poisonous qualities in the species that bear them, our poisonous plants are really relatively few, and even these are usually so disagreeable to the taste, or repellant in odor, as to prevent the average individual from being harmed by them. This fact cannot be too strongly emphasized, for the number of people who hesitate to visit the woods and fields, or who avoid handling strange plants for fear of being poisoned, is unusually large. To all such it should be a relief to know that there are only two plants in Eastern America that are poisonous to the touch, and even these are harmful to a few of the more susceptible only. To be sure, some people are poisoned by ordinary plants— radish leaves, okra pods, moccasin-flower stalks and leaves—and the various nettles spare none who come in contact with their

116

stinging hairs, but usually it is quite safe to handle such wild plants as we choose.

The only common species in our flora that poisons by contact, is the poison ivy (*Rhus toxicodendron*). This is the familiar climbing vine with leaves consisting of three leaflets, found in almost any woodland and conspicuous enough to be easily avoided. The other poisonous plant belongs to the same family, but its preference for deep bogs makes it unlikely that the average rambler will ever see it. This last is the species commonly known as poison sumach (*Rhus vernix*), but it goes under so many aliases that it appears to be a host in itself. Other terms for it are poison oak, poison ash, poison elder, poison dogwood, and poison tree.

Plants that cannot be eaten without harm are much more abundant. Some, indeed, are deadly poisonous. Nor are these all strange and seductive species lurking in the deep forests, ready to harm the unwary. Many are common plants of the garden and fencerow, such as elder, lily-of-the-valley, moonseed, datura, larkspur, aconite, water hemlock, and the like; in fact, there is probably a higher proportion of poisonous plants in the flower-garden than there is afield.

One of the commonest epithets applied to plants even suspected of being poisonous is *bane,* which word, or one of equivalent sound, means murderer in most of the languages of northern Europe. The bane-berries (*Actaea alba* and *A. rubra*) are really poisonous, but the poison-berry (*Solanum dulcamara*), though not edible, in many respects belies its name. Some of the banes we may even look upon with a tolerant eye, since they are reputed to drive away the animals for which they are named, especially the flea-banes (*Erigeron*), the bug-bane (*Cimicifuga racemosa*), the rat's banes (*Goodyera pubescens* and *Chimaphila maculata*), and the wolf's bane (*Aconitum napellus*). The dog-banes (*Apocynum*), must have been named on suspicion, since they are outside the dog's circle of acquaintances. It may be doubted whether any of the common dogbanes are poisonous at all. The plants have doubtless been mistaken for the fool's parsley (*Aethusa cyanapium*) of Europe, a deadly species, whose specific name refers to the dog. This was probably the original dogbane! The herb-bane (*Orobanche minor*) is another species that is not poisonous. The horehound (*Marrubium officinale*) is occasionally known as hound's bane. It is, however, a healing herb and not poisonous to dogs or other animals.

Henbane and hog-bane seem all the same to the namer of plants who thus translates the generic name, *Hyoscyamus*. The word, however, really means hog-*bean* but the plant is poisonous enough to deserve any name given it. The cow-bane (*Oxypolis rigidor*) does not seem to be baneful, but the spotted cow-bane (it is the plant not the cow that is spotted) is very poisonous and is otherwise known as water hemlock (*Cicuta maculata*). From the fact that children are sometimes poisoned through eating the white crisp roots in spring, this is also the children's bane. A related species, also spotted, is the poison hemlock (*Conium maculatum*), the plant that was used to put Socrates, the Athenian philosopher, to death.

A number of plants are known to be poisonous to stock, notably the green milkweed (*Acerates viridiflora*), the stagger-bush (*Lyonia mariana*), the lamb-kill (*Kalmia angusti-*

folia), and the cow-kill (*Eleocharis tenuis*).
There is also the kill-weed (*Lythrum sali-
caria*) which at first glance appears to be a
terrible species, but which is quite harmless
and in all probability is named for the kills
or creeks along which it delights to dwell.
Among the poisonous plants should probably
be placed certain species known as crazy-
weeds, from their causing symptoms akin to
insanity in stock that eat them. Three of the
best known are *Crotalaria sagittalis, Astragalus mollissimum,* and *Oxytropis Lamberti.*
The last two mentioned are famed as loco-
weeds and cause the death of many cattle
annually.

In the early days, when a favorite method
of getting rid of an undesirable individual
was to poison him, a knowledge of poisonous
plants was of more importance than at present. Many were the efforts made to discover a
good poison-detector. Mithridates the Great,
last king of Pontus, is given credit for the
brilliant idea of taking poison in increasing
doses daily until he was immune to any poison
a careless attendant might spill into his food
or drink. His case, however, illustrates the
evils of over-training, for later, desiring to

commit suicide, he found it to be impossible by the use of poison. Since his day, anything designed to counteract poison has been known as a mithridate. Two of our plants, *Lepidium campestre* and *Thlaspi arvense,* both emigrants from Europe, bear the name of mithridate mustard, but both are quite impotent, as might be inferred. *Thlaspi arvense* is also called treacle-wort because, like the treacle mustards (*Erysimum cheiranthoides* and related species), it was among the seventy-two ingredients used in making Venice treacle, a concoction that during the Middle Ages was regarded as a cure for "all those that were bitten or stung by venomous beastes, or had drunk poison, or were infected with the pestilence." The Latin word, *theriaca,* once meant a small animal, especially a viper, and when vipers finally came to be added to this kind of a mithridate, its name was changed to *theriake* and ultimately became treacle. We even have a treacle-berry of our own in the fruits of *Smilacina racemosa.* Josselyn reported that the berries taste much like that semi-fluid sweet which we call molasses but which in the Old World is still more commonly known as treacle.

CHAPTER XIV.

MEDICINAL NAMES.

Judging from the number of plants in our flora whose names indicate healing qualities, or which specify diseases that they are supposed to be "good for," it is apparent that the early settlers really "enjoyed poor health," as they used to phrase it. Illnesses and injuries are usually all too common in a new country and proper nursing and adequate medical aid difficult to obtain. It was quite natural, therefore, for the pioneers to cast about for healing plants of the region, and no doubt they were not averse to trying the potency of those Indian medicines which, in addition to such natural curative powers as they happened to possess, were invested with a certain amount of mystery and magic by the savages who compounded them. Even in a more enlightened age, various nostrums have derived much of their reputation for efficiency from the fact that they were discovered by an "Indian Doctor."

122

The Indian medicine-man, though totally unacquainted with technical science, was probably a fair botanist with a considerable knowledge of useful plants, especially those employed as remedies for common illnesses. Like his white brother, he doubtless placed reliance on many herbs of no medicinal value, but when several kinds were brewed together, the excellences of some covered up the deficiencies of others and gave a certain virtue to all. In any event, the white man's *materia medica* has been enriched by a number of plants whose value was first discovered by the Indian. Among species of acknowledged medicinal qualities are the Indian physic (*Gillenia trifoliata*), pleurisy-root (*Asclepias tuberosa*), and the bear-berry (*Arctostaphyllos uva-ursi*). There are at least half a hundred plants in our country that were on the Indian's list of curative agents, and most of these may still be employed in medicine on occasion. Included in the list are such common plants as elder, iris, boneset, bloodroot, wintergreen, chestnut, gentian, wild geranium, golden seal, blue cohosh, black cohosh, and pipsissewa.

The bitter principle in plants was early

recognized as tonic, and various concoctions known as "bitters" were once extremely popular. Bitter plants were regarded as especially useful in the malarias so common in new countries. Probably the favorite remedy for "chills and fever" or "fever and ague" was a mixture of quinine and whisky. This was often taken in anticipation of an attack and continued long after the patient had recovered—doubtless with a desire to prevent a recurrence of the trouble—or perhaps on general principles.

The most famous of the bitter plants of the domestic materia medica was the boneset (*Eupatorium perfoliatum*) which was gathered at the time of blooming, in late summer, and hung in bunches from the attic rafters along with horehound, peppermint, pennyroyal, and many other plants, against a time of need. A cup of the bitter tea brewed from the boneset, even if it did not cure, was calculated to make the patient forget all else for a time at least. Among other plants reputed to be a cure for malaria were the ague-root or ague-grass (*Aletris farinosa*), the ague-weed (*Gentiana quinquefolia*), and the ague-bark or

quinine tree (*Ptelea trifoliata*). The latter,
however, is not the species from which the
true quinine is obtained. As for plants called
bitterweed, there were at least half a dozen,
the turtle head (*Chelone glabra*) being a conspicuous example. There were, in addition,
other plants known as bitter-bloom, bitter-
buttons, bitter-herb, bitter-plant, and bitter-
wort. If none of these were effective, there
were still the fever-twig (*Celastrus scandens*),
the feverwort (*Eupatorium perfoliatum*), and
the wild quinine or feverfew (*Parthenium in-
tegrifolium*). The last name is a corruption
of *febrifuge* which might be translated as
fever chaser.

A number of the ancient plant names recall
afflictions which have happily gone quite out
of style, if not out of the physician's vocabulary. It may even require a resort to the dic-
tionary to interpret some of them. In the list
are salt-rheum weed (*Chelone glabra*), itch-
weed (*Veratrum viride*), scurvy grass (*Bar-
barea verna*), abscess root (*Polemonium rep-
tans*), tetter-wort (*Sanguinaria Canadensis*),
honewort (*Cryptotaenia Canadensis*), phthis-
ic-weed (*Ludwigia palustris*), pestilence-root

(*Petasites vulgaris*), fit-root (*Monotropa uni-flor*), small-pox plant (*Sarracenia purpu-rea*), mortification root (*Althaea officinalis*), consumption weed (*Pyrola Americana*) and cancer weed (*Salvia lyrata*). There were at least three scrofula plants (*Helianthemum Canadense, Goodyera pubescens,* and *Scroph-ularia marilandica*), and two other cancer-roots (*Thalia uniflora* and *Conopholis Amer-icana*). The canker-root (*Coptis trifolia*) or mouth-root, as it is called, belongs to a different order and continues to hold its place among medicines for the cure of sore mouth.

To list all the diseases that our plants have been reputed to heal would be to set down practically all the afflictions with which the medical man is familiar. Many of these are now known to be useless, but their names continue in our speech as mute witnesses of a time when they were in high repute. Others are mildly tonic or possess some faint medicinal value, but have long ago been superseded by more powerful remedies. Familiar examples are asthma-weed (*Lobelia inflata*), dysentery weed (*Lappula Virginica*), convulsion-weed (*Monotropa uniflora*), cough-root

(*Trillium cernuum*), purging-root (*Euphorbia corollata*), Kidney-root (*Hepatica Americana*), gravel-weed (*Diervilla trifida*), back-ache-root (*Liatris spicata*), headache-plant (*Anemone pulsatilla*) and belly-ache root (*Solidago bicolor*).

In addition to other plants of undoubted medicinal value, may be mentioned some of less efficiency, such as the colic-weed (*Dicentra cucullaria*), the various colic-roots, especially *Dioscorea villosa, Asarum Canadense,* and species of *Liatris,* the emetic-weed (*Lobelia inflata*), and the cramp-bark (*Viburnum opulus*). Six plants are called ipecac and none of them is the true one. They have effects similar to the regular drug, but are rarely used. The two more important of these are *Gillenia trifoliata* and *Triosteum perfoliatum*.

A few plants have been named for the diseases they cause or are reputed to cause. Most famous of these is the hay-fever plant (*Ambrosia artemisaefolia*). This species undoubtedly causes hay fever in susceptible people, but perhaps a hundred other plants do likewise and escape, while *Ambrosia* alone bears the stigma. We have two sneezeweeds, one,

Helenium autumnale, so called because it causes a sort of distemper in horses and cattle, and the other, *Achillea ptarmica,* because its leaves were once powdered and used as snuff. The milk-sick plant (*Eupatorium rugosum*) is an abundant wild species that is often introduced into the flower garden, but on the farm it frequently causes a disease in cattle known as "trembles" and produces in human beings who use the milk from such cattle, an affection known as milk-sickness which is often fatal. In some States, it is unlawful to allow this plant to grow on one's property.

Some plants have been so regularly used by certain individual medical practitioners as to have become indissolubly connected with their names. This is the case with Tinker's weed (*Triosteum perfoliatum*), Thompson's-root (*Lobelia inflata*), Bowman's root (*Gillenia trifoliata*), and DeWitt's snakeroot (*Prenanthes virgata*). It is likely that Sampson's root, (*Echinacea angustifolia*) commemorates another medical man, but it certainly was not named for the famous Israelite who seems to have done much better in his profession with the jaw-bone of an ass. We may also recall in this connection, the Indian doctor, Joe Pye, who is still remembered for his use of the Joe-pye-weed (*Eupatorium purpureum*).

Possibly the most interesting of the medicinal plant names are certain terms, mostly of exotic origin, which have descended to us through the Doctrine of Signatures. This Doctrine, brought to perfection by a Swiss alchemist, Bombastus Paracelsus, who was born about the time our country was discovered, was based upon the absurd assumption that Providence had placed a sign or "signature" on every plant to indicate the diseases it was able to cure. A plant with red juice was naturally good for the blood, round fruits, like the walnut, were specific for troubles of the head, plants with swollen joints like the pinks, a cure for gout, and so on.

The first names in this remarkable scheme were applied to the plants of Europe, but the doctrine was applicable everywhere and has resulted in some very misleading names. In our own flora is the jaundice-berry (*Berberis vulgaris*), so called from its yellow wood, the liverwort (*Hepatica Americana*) named for the color of the undersurface of its leaves and

not for its lobed leaves, as is often assumed,
the heartweed (*Polygonum persicaria*), which
has heart-shaped markings on the leaves, and
the eye-brights, ten in number, all good for the
eyes because the flowers have a lively and
wideawake appearance. The scarlet pimpernel
(*Anagalis arvensis*) and the species of *Veronica* are probably best entitled to the name
of eye-bright. Naturally nettle-tea was pre-
scribed for nettle-rash, several species with
spotted or mottled leaves were known as lung-
worts, and rough leaved plants were regarded
as cures for the itch and even for leprosy. The
Doctrine also has its representatives in the
technical names of plants, such as *Sanguinaria, Pulmonaria, Hepatica, Scrophularia,
Scabiosa,* and *Pedicularis.*

Not satisfied with plants able to cure one or
two diseases, our ancestors felt sure that they
had discovered several that might be regarded
as cures for "all the ills that flesh is heir to."
There were for instance, the nine-barks (*Hydrangea cinera* and *Physocarpus opulifolius*)
which may be assumed to have nine times the
efficiency of common barks, while *Hydrangea
arborescens* appears to be two barks short; at

least it was known as seven barks! The woundwort (*Stachys palustris*) was regarded as a cure for all sorts of wounds and the carpenter's herb (*Prunella vulgaris*) was so potent that it was known as self-heal and heal-all. The last named term was shared with half a dozen other plants, regarded as equally powerful, but their powers seem to have sadly degenerated with the passing years. There was also the ginseng (*Panax quinquefolia*) whose technical name was fashioned from the same word which gave us panic and panacea and which is still regarded as a panacea by the Chinese.

CHAPTER XV.

In the hop-growing regions of central New York, it sometimes happens that a vine, after climbing to the top of its support and finding nothing further to climb on, twines back upon itself, thus forming a loop which, in the rough and informal parlance of the hop-yards, is known as a "kiss-me-quick." The fortunate finder of such a loop is, by custom, permitted to kiss the lady of his choice through it as many times as the vine has made turns about itself—if the lady does not object. Thus does the hop, though once forbidden by Constitutional Amendment to contribute to the joy of convivial gatherings, retain its place with red ears of corn and sprigs of mistletoe as a promoter of good cheer and sociability and further substantiate the old adage that "where there's a will there's a way."

The hyphenated title given the hop-vine loop is by no means unique among plant

132

names. Our vernacular is full of such sesqui-
pedalian appellations, ranging all the way
from love-lies-bleeding and Johnny-jump-up,
to meet-her-in-the-entry-kiss-her-in-the-but-
tery, the latter, by the way, said to be the
longest plant name in the English language—
or probably in any other for that matter. Nor
are we unique in the possession of a kiss-me-
quick. England, indeed, has two; both bestowed, we are inclined to suspect, with less appropriateness, though probably serving the
purpose quite as well. The English bearers of
the name are a species of Saxifrage (*S. um-
brosa*) and the herb-Robert (*Geranium
Robertianum*), the latter an inconspicuous
little plant common to both sides of the Atlantic and, in England, often associated with
Robin Hood. The saxifrage also sports the
name of look-up-and-kiss-me or, as the term
has been expanded in some localities, look-up-
and-kiss-me-at-the-garden-gate. In England,
the finder of a kiss-me-quick is regarded as
lucky—as no doubt he is!

It is to be expected that unusual vernacular
names would be more common in the Old
World than in the new; the people there have

had more time to experiment in their making. But we are not far behind in such matters and have invented some on this side of the water that are quite as interesting and nonsensical. "Kiss-me-and-I'll-tell-you" replied an attractive native of the Southern States when asked the name of that plant which people of colder climes know as the daisy fleabane (*Erigeron anuus*). Whether this is really the name of the plant, or whether there is another name to be obtained in the manner indicated, shall remain a secret here since every true investigator will naturally wish to experiment for himself; the plant is wide-spread and abundant!

But lest it be assumed that all the polysyllabical names refer to matters of sentiment, we may turn to some that are concerned with more prosaic things. One of the common plants of our country waysides is a pretty species, with pink and white flowers, known as bouncing Bet (*Saponaria officinalis*). This was once an honored inhabitant of old gardens and prized for its showy blossoms, but proving too rampant and aggressive for the more refined garden folk, it was long ago turned out

to haunt the dusty roadsides in company with
other vegetable vagabonds.   With such company, however, it can never be quite in har-
mony, for, as its generic name indicates, it is
the soapwort, and soap, as everyone knows, is
abhorred by all sorts of vagrants.   It must
have been when it was in good standing with
the gardener that it received the pretty name
of lady-by-the-gate.   It is still entitled to the
name, though now, in reduced circumstances,
it lingers outside the portals that are forever
shut against it.

A number of other plants that produce handsome blossoms have nevertheless been disquali-
fied for a place in the garden because of their
too aggressive characteristics.   "A weed," it
has well been said, "is a plant out of place,"
and good garden plants, to avoid the gardener's displeasure, must know their places and
keep them.   Failure to observe this require-
ment has been the chief fault of the toad-flax
(*Linaria vulgaris*).   Unlike many of its low
associates, it did not enter the garden surrepti-
titiously.   It was imported for its tall spikes of
yellow and orange flowers.   No garden, however, is large enough for its ambitions and so

it was reluctantly cast out into the waste places. Unabashed by this turn in its affairs, it flounts its banners in a thousand fields where it is known as butter-and-eggs, eggs-and-bacon, bread-and-butter, and many another cognomen.

Associated with toad-flax and soapwort along many a roadside is the cypress spurge (*Euphorbia cyparissias*). It is a close-set little plant, much resembling an evergreen, and country housewives used to delight in planting it in some out-of-the-way corner. Left to itself, it preferred to form dense masses at the entrance of walks and drives, from which habit it is widely known as welcome-to-our-house. In these more degenerate days, it is seldom in position to welcome living guests, having been banished from the garden, but since it is an omnipresent species in old cemeteries, the name has acquired a sinister note which another of its appellations, graveyard-weed, only emphasizes.

Several other plants in our flora serve to remind us of life's vicissitudes. One of these, a species of loosestrife (*Lysimachia nummularia*) is called down-hill-of-life, and the water hemlock (*Cicuta maculata*) is death-of man. This latter species is poisonous enough to deserve its name, but it seems to have been confused with the poison hemlock, a still more poisonous species. A more agreeable side is given to the picture by that cheerful and persistent plant, the live-for-ever (*Sedun purpureum*) whose other name, life-of-man, makes plain who is to do the living.

A singularly appropriate title is that of lady-never-fade given to one of the cudweeds, *Anaphalis margaritacea*. This cousin of the edelweiss inhabits old fields and waysides and is also known as pearly everlasting and immortelle. Like a number of related species, commonly called straw-flowers, its blossoms have so little juice in them that when gathered the tissues lose what little moisture they contain without shrivelling or losing color, thus remaining unchanged in death, fit objects to bear the name of immortelle.

One of the inhabitants of the flower-garden that is steadily approaching that intangible line which separates the weeds from the flowers is the garden catchfly (*Silene armeria*), a plant which was anciently called pretty Nancy. This term, entirely meaning-less as it stands, when turned about and straightened up a bit, is none other than none-so-pretty. A plant so weedy and aggressive as this scarcely deserves so poetical a name. This, however, is not the case with the four-o'clock (*Mirabilis jalapa*) which bears the name of pretty-by-night and lives up to it. Its place in the garden is secure.

The four-o-o'clock and other night blooming flowers are always noticeable because they re-verse the usual custom of the plant world and bloom when other flowers are closed. Plants like the goat's beard (*Tragopogon pratense*), which close in the middle of the day, are equally remarkable. The promptness with which the goat's beard shuts its flowers when the sun has reached the meridian is astonish-ing. One might almost set his watch by it. It has long been known to children and country people as John-go-to-bed-at-noon, and was familiar to Old Gerarde, author of the Grete Herball, issued in the fifteenth century, who says of it "It shutteth itself at twelv of the clock and sheweth not his face open untill the next dayes sunne do make it flour anew, where-

fore it was called go-to-bed-at-noon.'' A cousin
of this plant, the vegetable oyster (*Tragopogon porrifolius*) has the same habit and in
consequence is often called nap-at-noon. The
star-of-Bethlehem (*Ornithogalum umbella-
tum*) also bears this title but without reason.
On the contrary it is so deliberate in opening
that it is called ten-o'clock-lady.

The little Venice mallow (*Hibiscus tri-
onum*), a weedy relative of the stately althaea
or Rose-of-sharon, takes the palm for floral
aberrations. It leisurely opens late in the
morning of fair days only, and closes scarcely
an hour later, being therefore most appropriately known as flower-of-an-hour and good-
night-at-noon. It is neither sunlight nor darkness that causes the blossoms of the little scarlet pimpernel (*Anagallis arvensis*) to open
and close during the day, but varying amounts
of moisture in the air. The flowers are exceedingly hygroscopic and close at the slightest hint of a storm, even though the sun is still
illuminating the heavens. Because of this
advance information of impending storms,
which is rather more accurate than the usual
weather forecast, the plant has long been

known as poor-man's-weather-glass, or occasionally as shepherd's-weather-glass. The fanciful name of wink-a-peep also alludes to this habit.

Perhaps more than half the seeds in the world are distributed by the bursting of the pods that contain them. In the tropics the sand-box (*Hura crepitans*) is the classic example, but on quiet autumn afternoons in our own region, one may hear the tiny guns of the plant artillery popping away in all directions. The New Jersey tea (*Ceanothus Americanus*) propels its seeds a thousand times their length and the witch-hazel (*Hamamelis Virginiana*) may do nearly as well, but in both of these one must watch and wait to see the explosion. Not so the jump-seed (*Tovaria Virginianum*). This has a trigger arrangement which needs only a touch to set things going. Similarly, the seed-pods of the garden balsam (*Impatiens balsamina*) burst open impatiently at the slightest touch, a fact which the generic name indicates. The plant has long been known as touch-me-not from the Latin *Noli-me-tangere,* but a more expressive name is the backwoodsman's quick-in-the-hand. Apparently this does not refer so much to the rapidity with which the seedpods explode as it does to the fact that it seems alive ("quick") in the hand that tries to grasp it. Our two common species of jewel-weed are well known for the same habit.

It is not with reference to these piping times of peace that the plant of old gardens known as honesty (*Lunaria biennis*) has been called money-in-both-pockets. The name is due to the fact that when the seeds are ripe, the walls of the capsule are so thin that the seeds are visible through them. It was inevitable that this plant should be called money plant, but matrimony plant is probably a misnomer in spite of the fact that money and matrimony are usually closely related. It was in reference to the two species of honesty that the botanist, Asa Gray, is said to have perpetrated a bit of sly humor in his "Field, Forest and Garden Botany." After the description of the first species he wrote; "common honesty; not native to the country but cultivated in old-fashioned places," and after the second; "perennial honesty, a much rarer sort seldom met with here."

There are two seasons of the year when flowers acquire an enhanced value in the minds of all. One is when the first warm days of burgeoning spring induce a few adventuresome blossoms to put forth in sheltered and sunny situations, and the other is when the mild days of Indian summer make a second spring and beguile certain belated blossoms into a feeling that the summer is not yet over. Among the first plants of the earlier season, is a little species of the parsley family, whose umbels of tiny pink-dotted flowers give it the name of pepper-and-salt (*Erigenia bulbosa*). Its more appropriate name, however, is harbinger-of-spring. Close in its wake come the spring beauty (*Claytonia Virginica*), just in time to make the name of good-morning-spring applicable. In the shrubberies, the fragrant honeysuckle (*Lonicera fragrantissima*) sends forth a perfume that may well make the name of first-breath-of-spring a tangible thing.

At the other end of the year, that anomaly among plants, the witch-hazel (*Hamamelis Virginiana*) or winter-bloom, which is either too late for one year or too early for the next, sprinkles its twig with yellow stars, but long before this the season has ended with the advent of the asters which are commonly known as frost flowers. Several species of this tribe are called fare-well-summer, and the new England aster (*Aster Nova Angliae*), which lingers long in the fields and fence corners, is further distinguished as last-rose-of-summer. When this plant blooms, the Indian surveys it soberly and sighs "It-brings-the-frost."

CHAPTER XVI.

Since there are more than seven hundred species of plants in eastern America that have come to us from foreign shores, it is evident that, paradoxical as it may seem, any list of American plant names must include a considerable number of European origin. Many of the plants that bear these names are now so completely a part of our flora that it is difficult to distinguish them from the indigenous species, and their names, of course, pass current in our common speech. Some of the more ancient, however, have been so changed by time and the transfer from one language to another that their origins and meanings are now a matter of conjecture, and the best we can say of them is that they are probably correct. A few of the more curious and devious ways in which they have descended to us may be considered here.

The word rocket is a term familiarly ap-

144

plied to more than twenty different species in our country. The plant with which the name seems to have originated is a small yellow-flowered annual, often cultivated abroad as a salad plant and known technically as *Eruca sativa*. The generic name seems first to have been corrupted to *ruchetta* by the Italians, further distorted to *roquette* by the French, and finally shortened to rocket by the British. A relative of the rocket, the common and homely cabbage, has a name whose derivation is equally interesting. We commonly speak of a head of cabbage, but since cabbage, itself, comes from the Latin *caput* meaning a head, our expression is a bit redundant. From the same word is derived capital, captain, and similar words. The French changed *caput* to *cabouche* and from this the English derived cabbage.

Both cabbage and rocket are members of one of the larger plant families whose flowers are distinguished by having four petals borne in the shape of a cross. It is commonly supposed that the word cress, applied to members of this family, is derived from the Latin word *crux,* meaning a cross. This, however, is a mistake; although the various species are generally called crucifers or cross-bearers. Cress is a very ancient term of different derivation. In the languages of northern Europe, it is spelled cresse, kresse, cerse, kers, ect. Incidentally it may be said that the old expression "not worth a curse" or "cuss" was originally "not worth a cerse" and carried no stronger implication than that the thing mentioned was of little value.

One of our native species, common also in Europe, has long been known as meadow-sweet (*Spiraea salicifolia*) and is usually assumed to have been named for the additional beauty and fragrance which its feathery trusses of flowers add to the meadow. The name, however, has no reference to meadows. Dr. Prior, the famous authority on plant names, insists that the plant is meadow-sweet because it was formerly added to mead—fermented honey and water—in the belief that it would impart to the beverage "the flavor of Greek wines." If this be true, the English plant is better flavored than our own, for ours never could come up to the specifications. It is likely, however, that after a few cups of the beverage it was supposed to flavor, the absence of any resemblance to Greek or other wines would not be noticed.

Practically the only pennyroyal we know of in America is a little plant of the mint family (*Hedeoma pulegioides*) which inhabits dry hillsides and makes its presence known, when trod upon, by a strong aromatic odor. The European species, *Mentha pulegium,* is the original pennyroyal, but our plant so closely resembles it in many essential features that the name is naturally attached to it. The specific name of both plants has reference to the flea (*Pulex*) from which the plants were supposed to be a protection. From *pulegium,* the specific name of the European plant, the common name gradually changed to *puleum,* then to *pulial* or *puliol,* and finally to pennyroyal. The oil is regarded as a defense—if such there be—against mosquitoes, and it may be equally effective against fleas, but no evidence is forthcoming on this point.

The name of Jerusalem artichoke is commonly given to one of our sunflowers (*Helianthus tuberosus*) but it has no reference to Jerusalem, even if the cooks do make Palestine soup from its edible tubers. The term comes from the Italian name for the plant—*girasole articiocco*—in which girasole means a plant which turns with, or toward, the sun. The English words turnsole and heliotrope have the same meaning. Our sunflower, however, does not follow the course of the sun through the heavens and is therefore neither a girasole nor turnsole. Its name of sunflower might be assumed to have reference to its turning toward the sun, but the name is really due to the appearance of the flower-heads, like the conventional figures of the sun. It is doubtful if any flower turns toward the sun all day, but another turnsole (*Euphorbia helioscopia*) has a specific name that indicates that it does.

Two species of wood-sage (*Teucrium canadense* and *T. scorodonia*) also bear the name of germander. At first glance the latter term is a mystery, but it is suspected that it is merely a corruption of chamaedrys, a word meaning dwarf oak and used for numerous specific names. Another word whose derivation is equally roundabout is betony, given to a little plant more familiarly known as lousewort (*Pedicularis Canadensis*). Betony seems to originally have been *Vetonica,* with reference to the Vetones, a people of Spanish origin. In the Latin the word became *Betonica,* in English *betony,* and in the parlance of the unlettered, *bitney.* Our plant, however, is not rightfully entitled to the name. This belong to *Betonica officinalis* of Europe.

A rough little plant, often grown in old-fashioned gardens and now escaped to roadsides and other waste grounds, is the borage (*Borago officinalis*). Its common name is often stated to be derived from *burra* a shaggy coat, but others believe the word to come from the Latin *cor* meaning a heart. It certainly was once known as *corrago* and probably became borago by the substitution of an initial B. In support of the latter derivation we have the old belief that drinking a decoction of borage gives heart (courage). An ancient writer observes that "If it be taken steeped in wine, all thy dearest friends may die and thou wouldst not grieve." It may be questioned, however, whether it is the plant or the method of taking it that is responsible for one's failure to grieve at the loss of his dearest friends. It is significant that still another of the plant's names is cool-tankard! Still, the plant must possess some virtues if it is true, as stated, that borage in one's shoes "prevents him from being tired at all."

The plant most commonly connected with the cup that cheers is the mugwort (*Artemisia absinthium*). It has the distinction of giving a name to two beverages of undoubted potency: Absinthe, a liquor flavored with its bitter leaves, and vermuth, a strong wine similarly flavored. Our plant is more commonly called wormwood and once had a reputation for repelling moths and their larvae. Wormwood, however, is often said to be derived from *vermond* or *waremood* and translated as "preserver of the mind," but, in view of the beverages with which it is associated, we may perhaps doubt it. Another guess at the meaning of *vermod* insists that *ver* means to keep off and *mod* is an ancient word for worm, which makes it possible to call our plant wormwood, though it is literally keep-off-worm. That mugwort also means wormwood is easily proved by the juggler of ancient terms. In Old English *moghe* or *moughte* certainly means a moth or maggot and thus mugwort becomes mothwort. But the end is not yet, for the plant was anciently known as motherwort, the name also derived from *moughte*. Examples such as this show what unstable foundations may underlie our common names.

A rather insignificant member of our flora is the rosaceous plant known as herb bennett, or as the older form of the name has it, *herba benedicta* or blessed herb (*Geum strictum*). The plant is indigenous to both sides of the world but its reputation for sanctity was acquired across the water. In confirmation of its claims to miraculous powers, it is said that "if the root of the plant be in the house it renders the devil powerless against it." Our plant, however, like so many others, trades on the reputation of a more powerful species, for the name of blessed herb really belongs to *Geum urbanum* of Europe—at least it is this species whose flowers and leaves were often carved on the pillars and facades of churches in the ancient days.

Few if any of the plants of our fields and woods have attained a greater reputation for potency than the common vervain (*Verbena officinalis*). It was anciently called holy herb and herb-of-the-cross and, as its generic name indicates, was one of the *verbenae* or sacred herbs used by the Romans in their religious rites. Although of no particular efficacy it has continued to enjoy a reputation as a powerful herb and is still called simpler's joy by the herb-gatherers. The plant was occasionally known as herb-of-grace, but the plant really entitled to this name is the rue (*Ruta graveolens*). From the earliest times this plant was regarded as a magic herb, able to confer second sight on its possessor and useful in all sorts of conjurations. In some places it was called countryman's treacle, in the belief that it would protect from poisoning. In later years, it seems to have dropped some of its associations with the powers of darkness, for it was used by the early missionaries for sprinkling holy water, whence the name herb-of-grace. We still use rue as a symbol of repentance and the expression "to rue" a thing is well known.

One of our most pestiferous weeds (*Amaranthus reflexus*) bears the sentimental name

of floramor or flower of love.   An inquiry into
the origin of such a name develops the fact
that it has descended in some way to this plant
from a handsomer species of Europe, *Amaranthus tricolor*. The name, however, does not
mean flower of love.   The French have translated *Amaranthus* as *flor de amor* from *amor,*
love, and *anthos,* flower, and some of the dictionaries have followed them in this, but the
real significance of *Amaranth* is never fading.
According to Prior, "the crown of glory that
never fadeth" mentioned in the Bible is, in
the original, "the amarantine crown of glory."

   The clove pink (*Dianthus caryophyllus*)
appears to have derived its name from the
clove tree (*Caryophyllus*) because of its clove-
like fragrance, but it is difficult to believe that
another of its names, gillyflower, is derived
from the same source.   This, however, seems
to be true when we examine more ancient
forms of the name and find that *Caryophyllus*
has been changed to *garyophyllus,* then to
gyllofer, from which it is but a step to gillyflower.   Our plant is the well-known carna-
tion, the name being often derived from the
Latin *carnis,* flesh, in allusion to certain pale

varieties. This, however, is an explanation similar to those which ignorance is wont to make in an attempt to fit the facts. The plant has always been a favorite for garlands and coronals and the specific name was anciently *coronaria* in allusion to such uses. Various other plants have the same specific name for the same reason. The fragrant dame's violet (*Hesperis matronalis*) has also been called gillyflower, but apparently through a misunderstanding, or because of its fragrance. Its more frequently used common name, however, has had an interesting series of transformations. It was once known as Damask violet (*Viola Damascena*) from Damascus in Syria, but the French term, *Violette de Damas,* was mistaken for *Violette des dames,* and so we have dame's violet. The plant is not a violet but in the days when the common name was bestowed, the word violet did not have the restricted meaning it does at present. Parkinson called our plant *sciney,* doubtless from a misunderstanding of *Damascena.* This term is not unlike *dame's scena* whence *sciney.* The double form of the flower was therefore called by the ridiculous name of *close sciences.* All this on the authority of the good Doctor Prior.

The early history of plant names is full of the curious changes that have befallen them. Those that happen to concern our plants are almost invariably attached to exotic species that have managed to get a root-hold on our continent. Even a list of these would be too long for inclusion here, though it everywhere offers points of departure for excursions into the realms of linguistics. We can merely add here a few of the more significant. To begin with, the word wine has probably been derived from a root *vi* meaning to bind or twine around, hence *Viburnum, Vinca* the periwinkle, and *Vitis* the vine. Wine is easily derived from the vine, both literally and literarily. Our pungent little plant, the dittany (*Cunila Origanoides*) in some way has acquired the name of a more important species of Europe, the gas plant or fraxinella (*Dictamnus fraxinella*), so called from its growing on Mt. Dicte in Crete. Tansy is from the French *athanasie,* the name of the plant in ancient times which is said to mean immortality. The modern generic name *Tanacetum* means literally, a bed of tansy. Snap-dragon

(*Antirrhinum*) is reported to be really sneb-dragon and means snout of the dragon, which the seed-pods resemble. This is more apparent when the ripe seed-capsules are examined. The *Veronica,* referred to by the poet as speedwell, in the line ''the little speedwell's darling blue,'' gets its name from *vera icon,* the true image, referring to the legend that the napkin with which Christ wiped his face on the way to Calvary retains his likeness. It was given to St. Veronica, the protector of our plant. The name of speedwell refers to the transitory nature of the flowers. The forget-me-not is the subject of another legend, but it appears that many, if not all, of our forget-me-nots are named for some unpleasant quality of taste or odor which impresses itself on the memory. Bittersweet has a similar significance, at least the technical name *dulca-mara* comes from two Latin words meaning sweet and bitter, in which the sweet comes first, as it does in so many of the plants bearing the name and alas, as it often does in human affairs.

INDEX

157